SPOON Fed

PubliBook IRELAND

Front cover by Julie Williams/Just Jules

ISBN: 978-1-909774-29-2

Published in 2016 by **PubliBook Ireland**
5 Cranbrooke – The Grange – Newcastle Road
Lucan, Co. Dublin K78 T889, Ireland

A CIP Catalogue record for this book is available from
The British Library and the Irish Copyright Libraries.

Designed, typeset, printed and bound in Ireland by **PubliBook Ireland**

PubliBook IRELAND

www.publibookireland.com

SPOON Fed

chris dina NIXON

Margaret Rose – Julia Bernadette

Content

PART I

One

As the day recedes small sounds run the hallway like mice.

Each footstep or cry has a troubled owner.

There is the sound of prayers and threats in equal measure carried through the dim light.

Tormentors become flesh and stand next to beds.

A challenge to the persecuted to call out.

Shadows fading into walls when night staff come to calm the defeated.

Laughter chokes reason and is issued with a punch line.

I lie here and think of all the ways I could have killed myself.

Morning is a long way off.

Monica tips the contents of one of her bags onto the floor, she's always searching for something.

She spills names and curses along with papers, tissues and pens.

Edith gets up and walks quietly from the room.

I used to follow her but it is too disturbing to watch as she fills each toilet and her mouth with paper.

She is only nineteen years old and already destined to belong here.

Some nights she finds another way to cut herself.

Teeth marks display where she has bitten through her flesh.

Her arms and legs crisscrossed with scars.

Wounds old and some still healing.

She is pointed out to the 'Bed and Breakfasters', those who come to us overnight with sore undressed wrists and hangovers of alcohol and panic.

"Fuck sake, that's the way to do it." Someone will say as Edith passes by, her past never covered and openly on display.
She smiles.
She has a place.
She believes she belongs here.

I am here because of how simple it is to believe and live a lie.
Here because it is easier to be Spoon Fed and swallow a reality than listen.
I have always known that I would come.
That silver coins would change hands and I would choke on others' betrayal.
Here because;
Because I saw my first colour television when I was nine years old.
It was at my aunt's house.
She had four children, all boys, the eldest a couple of months younger than me.
That Sunday afternoon we played upstairs.
All of us.
We ran up and down the long dark landing, shoulders and elbows kissing walls.
Feet thundering on old floor boards that sprang and roared back.
Banging in and out of bedrooms, doors slammed on fingertip shadows.
All surfaces were fair game, beds, lockers and dressing tables.
We nimbly stepped and jumped the distance to the next island or safe foothold.
The air dirtied by screams, filled with words of our own making.

Catching each other, hiding, laughing.
The game changed.
We split into two teams.
Them and Us.
The bedroom door closed.
I lay down and she positioned my legs.

8

My knees were touching the first time she pushed something inside me.

A key.

The key to an old wardrobe somewhere else upstairs in the house. Its twisted design denoted a grandeur that wasn't there. It looked as though it already knew secrets and should belong in children's games.

Real games.

I didn't move.

Around me smells that had made their way up the stairs and stubbornly remained to bleed their staleness. The carpet smelt of dust, damp, and the piss and vomit of young and sick children. It was cheap nylon with bright colours swirling like paint flicked from a brush.

It was harsh against my skin.

There was no underlay and the floorboards beneath that had earlier willingly rebounded under our feet became hard and disinterested. The room was untidy.

Our true games had left blankets to trail onto the floor. Pillows appeared mashed and spewed from their cases. The high ceiling was one of the few things in that room that was where it was meant to be.

Thin curtains pulled unevenly across the window allowed mute daylight to watch what she did.

She searched my body.

All part of the game, pretending her intrusion was to find the lost key.

Rapid fingers sought their prize.

It hurt.

I anchored my shoulders to the floor to stop the coarse movement of my body as fingers violated further inside me.

She stopped, the key discovered.

I watched as she smelt it and held it up for us to see, like an offering, the Host, a trophy. Her face alive and smiling as she bragged of the great hiding place she had found.

She parted my legs.

I lay silently.

Her game not quite over.
Now aware that skin could be manoeuvred.
Squeezed and pinched.
That it had different tastes.
Provided a pleasure.
Satisfied need.
Vanquished.
I turned my head and my little brother stared at my face.
He never moved or spoke.
She hadn't thought up a part for him.
Yet.
Time slowed, just as it would for the rest of our childhood when she touched me.
She talked excitedly of when we would be older.
"Grown-ups."
The name she awarded the future us.
We would live together, the three of us.
I lay on the floor beneath her and agreed with her rules.
There was no mention of truth, shame or this place in her vision.
How did she know that I wouldn't shout?
That I wouldn't tell when we left the game?
Was it the first time?
We heard the others running, shouting they weren't playing with us anymore.
Their voices fading as they left the upstairs.

Later, downstairs, amongst the others and our parents we reverted to the children we outwardly still were, and presented the relationship expected.
We all sat and watched the new television, plates balanced on our knees and glasses of weak orange squash on the floor near our feet. A war film entertained and we saw blood on the wounds of the fallen soldiers. Everyone said how real colour made dying look.
I was sore and uncomfortable when we left in the dark for home.
Our little brother sat between us in the back of the car and she ignored us.
He never spoke, spinning the wheels of a truck with his thumb.

She leaned forward, filling the space between the front seats and chatted to our parents.

They didn't know what their three children had become.

That the three of us had a secret now.

A secret we had to keep.

A secret that would grow stronger, more vengeful and shadow me into madness.

My little brother didn't know the secret that my sister and I already had.

We had played a game before.

On the bed in the spare room.

She had called me in and closed the door.

Said this was our game just her and I.

I lay on the bed with my legs parted and arms outstretched above my head.

I was supposed to be a prisoner.

My hands clasped together pretending they were tied.

I had my clothes on the first time she touched me.

I didn't tell.

I was good at secrets.

I didn't tell them about the woman at karate practice what she did.

Two

Please let this be death.
I thought I heard a plane circling lower and lower.
The noise directly above me then gone.
I don't know if it was real.
Thoughts of Pearl Harbour and film I'd seen of Japanese pilots gliding to their mortality flipped through my mind.
I heard whistles.
Lots of whistles and my name being called.
I wished it were night.
Easier to be lost.
Unseen.
Just another shade amongst the trees.
Obsolete.
No body's business and guarding my own.
I didn't want anyone to rescue me.
I knew there were people nearby.
 I could hear their movements and calls.
I held my breath hoping not to be heard.
"Please go away."
Death doesn't grant wishes and now nasty adult fueled children taunt my daughter daily at school about her 'round-the-bend' mother.
I'd love to turn up and be the crazed they fear.
Jump from my car and shout ***"BOO"*** at her tormentors.
Leap across the playground wall and swing threateningly from the basketball hoop.

A demonic Lord of Greystokes.

Hiss venom and scatter children as I grab at their coats with razor sharp talons.

Screech with delight as they run terrified and unprotected below me.

No maternal wings to beat off their assailant.

Perch and watch the aftermath as whispering mothers make issue of their young and hear them condemn me for letting mine go.

That's one of their favourite fascinations and unanswered questions here.

They never tire of asking and it never varies.

Like junkies there is a daily need to be satisfied, a need for a sane answer, an answer that confirms they know best.

"Didn't you think of your child?"

"Yes."

All of the time.

If I hadn't thought of or considered her I would have hurt her.

All the time I sound her name.

Her face and voice plays unchecked through my mind and I battle to keep those images and my memories of her safely segregated from those that belong to me.

There is a voice inside me, a cruel one.

I was afraid that if I remained my daughter would hear it, that I would expose her to what awful things can be done.

I tried to stay sane.

It's hard, all but impossible to not eventually cave to the constant grip of ghosts and alter.

Suffer little children who come unto me.

Bang on.

Shouting.

Bad tempered.

Cruel.

I have been all of those things.

Almost the malicious older sibling.

I have no pride or defence.

But I know if a different past held sway I could have held my child as the person I wanted to be.

* * *

Everyone here carries something external with them. A plastic bag that's clutched and cared for like an infant.

The contents of a case itemized and rechecked throughout the day.

Empty pockets filled with need.

As though we all failed to protect ourselves from an insipid dismantling force. Forced now to compensate with D.I.Y and controlled secrets.

I have a green notebook and a Parker pen.

The nurse tries to make conversation from her chair.

"What are you writing?"

"Do you want to talk?"

Always questions.

I don't usually answer and turn myself on the bed to face the painted wall.

Making sure she sees my exaggerated push of the earphones of the iPod further into my ears.

I don't always switch it on and it serves to excuse both of us from trying.

I shower and piss with a companion.

I am not allowed to be on my own yet.

I have my own room but no sharp objects or sprays.

A single bed.

Comfortable.

Two chairs, one wooden, the other some sort of an attempt at comfort and style but failing at both, it's bolted to the floor.

A window that doesn't open and an empty wardrobe.

My clothes are locked away somewhere else.

Stored like valuables in a safety deposit box.

Each morning I am taken to a room full from ceiling to floor with locked cupboards of varying sizes.

It's always dim in the odd space.

Voices from the corridor are funneled in and sounds gather from the office and bathroom either side of the doorway.Shiny varnish darkened by time and no natural light dominate the realm and demands hushed voices and supplication. The nurse has a key that opens each of the cupboards.

One key, the same lock to dozens of doors.

From the first day people were locked in, these doors have held the simple belongings of people like me.

Strangers with just one address.

Each of the doors displays a tiny brass number.

7 has been allocated to me.

Has someone recently left or is it purposely mine?

I believe the number, distance above the floor, and closeness to the entrance holds a significance in their belief of how long I will remain.

Jackie calls this place **The Lost's' Luggage.**

From my case I take fresh underwear and pajamas, I'm not allowed to dress in what they jokingly term 'run-away' clothes. Getting them back, they tell me, should be one of my goals.

I put my dirty worn stuff into a yellow polythene bag that declares it's the property of this institution.

When open it smells of captivity.

Twice a week I send it home with my husband.

My name is written in blue ball point pen on sticky labels and fixed to anything that is mine.

The soles of my shoes, toiletries.

Even bags of crisps and sweets.

Phone chargers and all corded electrical goods are off limits to everyone and each morning I take my charger from the bag and give it along with the phone to a nurse who plugs it in whilst I eat breakfast.

Even though I have my own room the door is never closed, wedged open by a chair sat upon by the nurse who has drawn the short straw and spends her shift in documenting my movements, sleep and any hoped for outbursts or display of emotion or erratic behaviour.

I try to make her time as boring as possible.

No other patients are allowed into my room, some speak to me from the doorway and others stop and linger in the corridor openly watching the Special Care exhibit.

I write in this book and carry it everywhere with me.

My Doctor asked would I like to show it to the staff.

I told him **"No."** My hands pressing it tightly between them.

I have no doubt they would steal a peep if left out in the open unguarded.

If they could witness my ramblings how easy to categorise me.

This book is my way of talking to me.

My purpose, my reason, there is no safety for sanity inside my mind at this time.

Three

"Sorry if it hurts." He began to tap a pin into my skin.

Twenty years later I lay on the ground looking at my unnaturally white hands. Nails bitten, my short fingers misshapen as though submerged in water for a long time.

Frogs Feet my father had called them.

Hated when he or anyone made reference to the state of my fingernails but it didn't stop me biting. I no longer used the excuse of scratching my teeth and sought the pleasure at any moment of my day. At times it would be difficult to find growth and so to satisfy my need gnawing until my fingers bled.

My mother would pounce and smack my hand away from my mouth, then hold out wet fingers and again point out their ugliness compared to my sister's. I would suffer the vile taste of the clear varnish that she daily painted on. Spitting and wiping my tongue. My mother said my nails would begin to grow inside my stomach and push out through the skin. I didn't fully disbelieve her and sometimes stroked my stomach to make sure it was smooth. My sister ventured a cure for the habit, saying they should dip my fingers into cat shit and then push them into my mouth.

I knew she would willingly be the one to do it.

The woman at karate and The Brown Lady both had beautiful hands that they slowly moved when they spoke.

The woman's were always cold.

I could see my hands clearly as it was no longer night and early morning sunlight fell unbroken to the ground.

Breathing felt unimportant and I hoped I was dead.

Would a figure appear?

A God or Saviour to guide me home like we were taught to believe?

Nothing.

I was alone.

No trail of redemption flavoured breadcrumbs or markers to ease my transgression.

Getting to Heaven was far harder than just stepping in its direction.

Access to Hell had proudly boasted **No Restrictions.**

It had made certain of my passage and sent a lifelong chaperone to take my hand.

Gripping ever tightly and insisting I miss nothing.

How do you know if you are dead?

Trees crowded around, indifferent to the disgust and loathing that no physical force had dragged me up those narrow stairs to the bedroom we had shared.

My sweat pants were sodden, muddy.

I must have fallen sometime during the night.

From my surroundings I knew that I wasn't in the place I had lain down to die.

I closed my eyes.

When I awoke again disappointment secured itself within me and smirked.

Could I will my life to end?

I'd heard of and read about people who had died from broken hearts, loneliness, just given up, or lost-the-will-to-live.

How long did it that take?

I lay and watched rain water drip from the end of a fern.

It had rained for most of the night and morning.

Yawning branches released drops that fell to my face.

There was no annoyance or evil in their touch.

I didn't move or wipe them away.

Let them fall until I no longer noticed.

I was cold, a sort of numbness, but the sensation pleasurable.
Total.

One unifying feeling, no separate pain or misery. My body accepting this new silent code of perception.

The ground beneath me was soft and I knew if I remained it would take care of me.

If left undisturbed it would consume me, no malice in its need.

The smell of a thriving world of trees, growth and rot was loud. Resin glistened on bark and moss silently claimed a prize. Trees spaced by man reached for each other, their branches seeking companionship and intimacy.

The air felt like the cold water from a spring well and I knew I could stay here.

No need to whisper or speak I would not seek escape, happy to take this as my death.

I was unable to stand or lift my arms properly, the cuts on my wrists reopened and driveled blood with every move. I slumped like an aged puppet enslaved to snagged and twisted strings. My hands unable to coordinate with my legs the task of crawling. My head weighted as though held just above the earth with magnetic force. The imaginary pull coupling my face with the ground.

Hangover symptoms of what was a benign overdose.

All I wanted to do was sleep.

Just sleep.

Although I left my daughter behind I brought her with me.

I carried the key ring with her last school photo.

The first one she had smiled in.

She had hated school pictures as she was alone in them, all her friends had older or younger siblings and they gathered oldest at the back and smallest at the front, each year the same back drop of a mystical blue.

She said the photographer had said something silly to make her smile.

When she was born I knew I would have only one child. That no one close to her would harm her.

On the other side of the key ring a small picture I had trimmed to fit.

I had taken it of her and her father the rainy evening we'd had a picnic at the town lake. They held hands out in the water. She squealed and wriggled as he lifted her, one of her red boots slipping from her foot and landing in the water.

Coats and Crisps I called it.

It was a bitterly cold November evening and the water rose and broke in waves.

A spray hit us like rain.

Squealing we all shook ourselves like dogs that step back but inch forward in anticipation and hope that the water will still reach them.

There were big stones and concrete blocks thrown out into the water and we balanced on them.

The three of us went home with wet feet.

We battled Orcs with sticks we had gathered and beheaded invaders that had sailed the Seven Seas and Time in search of us. We heard hounds out hunting and imagined we were their prey. Escaping an evil kingdom. To us they weren't normal dogs but creatures formed in another World. They came thundering down the hill and through the trees. Their feet slipping unable to get proper grip. Some of them tumbled. We all jumped as they raced by uninterested in or distracted by our scents. They and their noise moved off into the distance and we pretended our stealth and cunning had prevented capture.

Bluebells performed everywhere and I wanted the two of them to help me collect the flowers. They both looked at me with surprise and disbelief at my complete waste of time.

I contrived a game that meant we had to gather food and potions and that the Bluebell roots were a prized source of energy and deadly poison. Each coming up with a hideous disfigurement or silly reaction caused by the drinking of the deadly brew. We would become wizards and casters of spells once we found a way of transforming the beautiful into the deadly. As tools we used sticks to dig the delicate flowers free from the ground. Bringing them home in our pockets and planting them beneath a sycamore tree across the road from our house.

They collapsed but revived and grow now every year, easily seen from an upstairs window.

I like to imagine they will spread unhindered as time goes by.

Four

I used to think that if she knew how I felt she'd have stopped it.
I remember what she said.
I remember because I loved her so much I did exactly as she told me.

Five

I know a woman who slashed her own throat.
She had seventy two stitches and almost bled to death.
Almost.
An impressive Halloween scar screams a challenge to imagine.
Did her hand hesitate or falter as flesh ceded?
Was the pain instant?
I have no idea.
I don't know how or why she did it.
I have never asked and she has never questioned me.
Honestly?
I don't care.
I don't know her name, and I don't think she knows mine.
She emerges and fades amongst the doorways further along the corridor.
In the first days I would bow my head slightly, moving eyes upwards to see her but soon became aware we were watching each other.
I am not even sure if she is real and I am afraid to ask.
Her movements are slow and gentle and if she speaks she whispers.
She only speaks to me.
Sometimes to ask the day or date.
Her breath not stirring the air.
I often wonder did she make a sound.
I always answer but there is no acknowledgement or interaction beyond the brief exchange.

There is something ghostly about her, as if maybe, maybe she did die, but is unaware she is now free to go.

Her skin is almost transparent. And, well, she's clean. Clean like something new, untouched and precious unwrapped from fine tissue paper.

Her long fingernails are each shaped to the same curve and each day they are freshly painted red.

An acetate aroma pushes before her and lingers when she has passed.

From early evening she wears soft slippers that brush and polish the floors and pristine night clothes that flow and ripple like the garments of a nineteen thirties movie star.

Could I have imagined her?

Or

Remembered her?

I know I taught her how to play Solitaire in the smoking room.

She stood, always watching.

Moving and standing closer and for a little longer each time that I played.

Her shadow tinted the small table as I laid out cards.

Without raising my head I asked;

"Would you like to play?"

She didn't speak, just moved and sat across the table from me.

I looked up and into her eyes.

"Teach me the game you play for the lonely."

She plays all the time now.

Alone.

Has her own deck of cards, keeps them in a dressing gown pocket.

As of the moment the cellophane was unwrapped from the around the pack no other hand has touched them.

She shuffles the cards quickly, a sound like the beat of a trapped bird's wings.

I see her moisten the tip of her thumb with the slightest touch of her tongue.

Counts cards and places them neatly on the table top.

Eyes darting over Suits and numbers.

This morning I asked if she knew any other card games, that maybe we could play together sometime. Her eyes lifted to mine and she dismissed me saying she didn't want to know any others.

I know lots of things.
That Hell is a place you would never find on your own;
The weight of the water held back by the Hoover Dam;
That there isn't any such thing as unbreakable clothes pegs;
How many folds to make the perfect paper plane;
I know how worthless Jack's cow felt to be sold for imaginary beans;
And,
I know why children never tell.

Six

It's raining now, heavy clouds seem to have made the mountains disappear.
I watch from the smoking room window to see if they will return before dark.
Every morning before breakfast I check if they are there.
They have been gone this time since early yesterday.
My nurse companion doesn't come in here, opens the door and tells me not to leave. Usually goes for a break and I am monitored through the glass by different sets of eyes.
I sign with my hands, head or lips when I am ready to leave.
I can remain in here for as long as I like.
Harsh rain decorates the window with distorted sounds and I wonder if I were to press my head hard against the glass would the cold water find its way inside and make everything brand new.
A clean start.
Different colours.
The pane is dirty and smudged with fingerprints and breath kisses.
There are traces of names and random swirls trapped within the memory of the greasy surface of the glass.
I can see cars move along the access road beyond the fence and students from the nearby Art College carry class projects and khaki bags. Each dressed with planned difference, their quest for uniqueness marking them instantly identifiable.
I pretend I know what they talk about.
I can hear voices and allotted accents.

I have given names to the familiar faces, and decided which of them I don't like.

I plot lives with crisis and casual happiness.

I know their problems, their dreams, and their blindness to what lies ahead.

I wonder how far my imaginings fall.

They never openly look towards here.

No eye contact with the demented.

But I've seen them.

They all peep.

An involuntary head movement called Curiosity.

If for some reason they have to walk on our side of the road they distance their bodies

from the fence, balancing their feet on imaginary stepping stones.

They never stand still to chat.

Belief that their moving feet will protect their sane thoughts from ensnarement.

They never see beyond the Health Board sign or these locked windows that covet their movements. I have no doubt that they each return to their homes, rented houses and amongst friends tell tales and college legends of contact with their insane neighbours.

I would.

We all do.

When visitors come we each quickly point out the contrast between ourselves and others' subtleties and madness.

No way could I be mistaken for any of them.

I can sit back and feel superior.

Pretend I would stand out from this crowd.

But I know that if one of my photography class from the art college chose us as a venture in study, bright orange coloured Nikes would be my only visible difference.

Maria once attended the art college, graduated to this side of the road with the aid and accompaniment of the sound track;

"Try this."

She has stopped crying and is happier this afternoon.

Says maybe she will get a frog.

"How would I know if it was the one to kiss?"

I wish I could give her the answer.

Seven

I know it is insane.
Telling myself things I already know.
But there is no place for everything inside my mind.
When I walk to the end of the corridor and feel that the nurse or no one else is watching, I bend and breathe the fresh air.
I must be swift as it races against the keyhole and hurtles inside.
Dragging lost sounds and smells across my grateful skin.
Gifting me glimpses of forfeited people and possessions lost to me beyond these doors.
Galloping through and whistling by in greeting.
An enthusiastic child released into a Fairground.
Quickly disappearing as it moves captive and unfettered amongst the beds.
It touches every space.
Each curve and scratch.
Feeling its indiscriminate way with excited curiosity along walls and bodies.
Then something happens, a piercingly silent moment when it appears to inhale surroundings and realise the mistake in being here.
Instantly becoming anxious and harsh with an animal need to escape.
Erratically drumming against windows, rushing across cold floors.
Searching and demanding release.
All it needs is the slightest gift to defy containment.
An opening.

A crack.

A grasped glimmer of hope and it is gone.

Quickly loosing scents of the broken lives it witnessed.

The opening in the keyhole is never empty.

A never ending game with no lessons learned.

Just think, the air that slaps coldness to the back of your neck may once have held our despair.

Held my breath.

Carried a lunatic's wish, prayer, curse or kiss.

The air though is canny and quick to appreciate that it doesn't belong here.

If Truth dealt in honesty it would have to admit that nothing belongs here.

Here?

A **Place of Safety** they like to call it.

A catchy label that makes the smug fuckers who came up with the meaningless phrase even smugger and pleased with themselves.

It allows them to walk more erect than you or I.

Enlightens those who are placed here just how worthless they have become.

Welcome to the Pleasure Dome.

My fellow inhabitants care little if anyone dribbles, whispers, re-mains mute or screams.

Here, you can be anything or anyone you want.

Invisible companion's uniqueness fades and they tend to rest in corners or out of sight. Always primed and ready.

It's your,

If you are really lucky,

Once-in-a-lifetime offer to embrace Madness.

Here you can walk on all fours and not be avoided because of odd behaviour.

We are right down in the scary darkness at the bottom of the rabbit hole.

Ungoverned by social niceties, half days or holidays.

So here I am.

A Mother.

A Protector.

Dream-catcher.

Hand-holder.

And Fear-chaser.

Behind doors that mostly remain locked.

Jackie says the quilt covers are colour coded.

A safeguard and alert for staff.

One quick glance and the truly insane are noted.

Light blue check has our vote and we watch closely our own bed linen.

Jackie is afraid of the dark.

She sleeps fully clothed, shoes laced or boots zipped.

Ready to run if her tormentors draw near.

On days when she wears no makeup, and fails to straighten her heavily dyed hair, I know night has won and she won't speak, eat or live for that day. Her stillness keeping her hidden, inactivity her believed tradeoff for a silent future night.

She is years younger than me, yet her skin and features appear as though they have been racing through time without her.

She has been here before, each time death or a solution has avoided her.

She says she no longer knows what she needs answered and sometimes wishes she could be dead just long enough for her family to miss her.

For just one person to miss Her.

Not the things she provides, cooks, washes or picks up.

In the smoking room she talks of an old style movie projector set up in her living room. No wild colours or interruptions as a silent movie plays of her life.

There would be no refreshments served or refunds given.

No one is allowed to leave their seats or turn away until the final clear image has faded.

Their tears she ignores, their mouths open and lips move but she defiantly waits.

She concedes no ground, her terms, and all concessions fall in her favour.

She laughs that sometimes it plays out and she sees herself as they all gain colour and perfect shape when they welcome her back, but mostly all remain still, colourless and nothing changes.

She, like most of us holds a dream in which she can be heard.

She, like all of us, knows that it is just that, a dream.

We have lost more than our minds in this game.

Place settings at tables and family gatherings no longer guaranteed.

Eight

I am not doing the school run today.

I won't be there tomorrow.

On the day I left I sat in my car outside my daughter's school and watched her playing. The preschoolers shared the playground and the voices of all the children fused into one sound and I couldn't find her words.

I wonder did she see me.

She never looked towards the car and none of her friends noticed me and said;

"There's your Mammy."

I would have waved.

I may have stayed.

I think.

Out loud and held within the car I said **"Goodbye."**

There was a whisper, I didn't have to strain to hear what was said, the voice was clear. **"Bring her with you."**

I had clothes and food in the back of the car.

Coats and Crisps.

The voice reminded me that I had everything she needed.

As a child I couldn't remember a time the woman hadn't been watching me.

My parents said she wasn't real, that lots of children made up and had an imaginary friend.

But I didn't imagine her.

She was real.

She was there.

My sister was four years older than me and we didn't play together very often and for some reason my parents saw the friend as something comforting.

They thought it cute as they asked me about her.

"What does she say?"

"Nothing."

"What does she look like?"

"I don't know, she's a woman."

"Is she like a ghost? Is she scary?"

"No, but she's sort of faded." Like a washed colour.

"Is she here now?" They would look for her as though peering through a dirty window.

"No."

She had no name but because of the odd colour she appeared to be I called her the Brown Lady.

She didn't play or harm me, she just stood and watched when I was alone.

She seemed indifferent to me, treating me as though I were the one who happened to be intruding into the other's world.

There was nothing of comforting kindness about her but she didn't scare me either.

When she began to speak I told them I no longer saw her.

Her quiet voice spilled random words and passages from children's books that I had read, but as my sister changed and became crueler the Lady became silent and then left.

She had cried when she saw the things my sister made my younger brother and I do.

As an adult and as my mind began to unravel I heard her voice again.

The first time was a day I was in the bank and the cashier was joking about not listening to her husband. Telling me she was looking forward to getting away with friends.

They were going to Helsinki for four days and I wished her well.

She counted out notes into my hand and as I lifted them she smiled, her mouth moved but it wasn't her voice. **"Any day your child is above ground is a good day."**
Familiar tone that I recognised from my childhood.

I think the Brown Lady had been jealous of the woman at karate practice.
She was the only person she ever questioned or asked me about.
The woman at karate practice had been beautiful too.
I loved going to karate, because my sister didn't go and my father dropped me and collected me afterwards. We'd secretly eat in the car and not tell anyone.
I went every Sunday morning and every second Thursday evening. It was held in the hall belonging to a church.
Sometimes during the Thursday session the adults watched films projected on to a sheet. Five boys around my age and I sat on steps or tried to hook our legs around a handrail and hang upside down out in the hallway. Out there it was always cold and not properly lit. That strange yellowy glow of security illumination that in my child's
mind most certainly was home to ghosts and evil.
I'd peep through the frosted glass of the door that divulged nothing but dampened light. Their laughter and silences shone through.
She watched the films too.
She was the only woman.
She wore lots of make-up, a black outline around her eyes like dark masking tape.
She pushed the tip of her tongue slowly between her teeth when she smiled.
The whole movement had an unnatural and practiced feel.
She'd tell me about the films they had watched. Sitting me down as if sharing a fairytale. Running her hands up and down my back as though trying to warm me.
The coldness of her hands detectable through the cloth of my karate suit.

She'd sometimes stand in front of me when we'd be changing out of or into our suits, her lips pursed as though about to blow a secret kiss. Then ask me did I like her "lingerie."

To me it did not look anything like proper underwear and seemed to be made of strings and frills.

She said I could touch.

It made a harsh sound and felt like the net curtains that hung in our bathroom window.

She asked me to stand still as she brushed my hair.

She told me I might be pretty.

I would think of her words when my sister would tell me that I was meant to be a boy.

Nine

Last Sunday when my husband and daughter came to visit, she asked why no one had broken legs or arms here.
"What sort of hospital is this?"
The people presented before her didn't exhibit symptoms of illnesses or bear visible wounds or display ailments that would be known to her.
I knew by her face she was questioning the stories her father, and others are telling.
"Your Mammy is in hospital."
I told her it is a place for people with tired minds.
My husband looked at me.
"Will it stop you shouting?"
She asked questions that no adult would.
Things that mattered to her...
Would it make me happy?
That if it did;
"It's a good idea and everyone should come for about." she paused.
"Eighteen days a year."
If not.
"Could you just come home?
Please."

When someone older visits I smile and joke, betraying the others around me in imitation and laughter. Depreciating their misery to keep the conversation easier, and no mention of why I am here.

That is never discussed, and openly avoided with the precision of a driver on ice.

I tell my visitors that it is not so bad, that it is a bit like a holiday without a pool or the sun.

I also tell them that I don't mind being here.

That is a lie.

One of the biggest ones I have told.

But it is what they want to hear.

I'm like a child who says **"Please"** and **"Thank you",** doesn't mean it, but also knows there are rules to the games.

I whisper to myself when my visitors have gone home.

"I hate it."

How smoke and mirrors the tacking on of the unpronounceable name of some obscure saint who felt affinity with the mentally deranged.

A lie, a clever delusion, a slight of hand.

All dressed up with seasonal flowers tended to in brightly painted tubs.

Carefully mown lawns and decked areas with picnic benches deliver ease for visitors and relatives to leave.

Visiting time is dressed, best china and cake stand in the parlour.

Grounds filled with Centuries old oak and mature copper beech with leaves that tease in movement and murmurs won't return my sanity.

Truth?

What I really believe but will never say to my husband's shipwrecked face?

This has to be the worst thing someone could do to or guilt another person into doing to themselves.

Take me away on holiday, anywhere, or just close the front door and fucking listen.

At least we would have been together.

I wore loneliness before but it is nothing compared to what prowls here.

I am again alone, alone to crawl through these emotions.

To face fears, make a stand and put Humpty back together.

I did nothing wrong,
I violated no body, yet I am the one to be pushed away and hidden.
If I speak it is to strangers who listen in ink.
Their purpose highlighting and underlining that I am on my own.
This is my problem, deal with it then come back.
Now all I share with my family is a separate shame.
I fill daily with more unheard words, disgust and hatred of myself.
My name is on a white board in the corridor and I am officially a Nutter.
Being here will stay with us forever.
As Jackie says, **"you can never not have been a psychiatric patient after you have been admitted, slept in the beds and sat at their tables."**
There is no key to hand back or deposit returned.
More taboo, something else to be avoided in conversation.
An aid to the raising of eye brows.
Nudge-nudge.
I'll always have a postscript.
"Did you know?"
"Her mother was..."
"His wife did..."
A touch that will tap me on the shoulder if I dare to enjoy laughter.
On guard in case my happiness is mistaken for madness.
This doesn't wash off.
Indelible markings of my failings and despair.

Ten

A hideous tattoo on my left arm confirms how monumentally stupid I was as at eighteen. I had finished school and had no full time job. I was the opposite of and continuously compared with my sister. Underachiever became my label.

My mother said I would find my place.

I really didn't care as my true ambition was just to leave.

My sister was deep in a relationship with the man she would ultimately marry.

They were both working and saving. She was beautiful, liked, with good manners and a sharp wit.

My brother mixed and joined every youth club and group. He competed and excelled in all sports. Worked in a garage in the evenings and at weekends.

He very much lived his own life popular amongst a wide group of friends.

Everything he did kept him from having to spend time at home.

Despite the deep hate I had for my sister part of me felt something else.

I loved her.

She was my elder sister and I envied what she was and what she had become.

Envied that she had left our past behind.

I think because it was over for her she believed it would likewise be for us.

My brother and I rarely spoke.
He never looked me in the eye and avoided being alone with me.
My sister hadn't touched me or forced my brother and I together from I turned seventeen.
There were two years between him and I.
Our avoidance of each other meant that the three of us rarely fought or argued. A state that my parents were happy with. Believing the bond of family responsible for our behaviour.
They willingly fed on the image.

I'd heard my sister say we had little in common.
In reality we had too much.
Although we no longer shared a room or touched, I was still cutting myself.

Had done it for the first time the night she brought our little brother into the game.

Had pushed the tip of a pair of scissors into the piece of webbed skin between my thumb and fingers, amazed and curious at how easy it was. A tiny mark of blood that spread and followed the grooves in my skin.
From then on I would use my father's double edged safety razor. Lifting it from the windowsill in the bathroom. The blades were disposable, little matchbox size packets were bought that contained five new blades. Each individually held within a tiny envelope displaying the maker's name
I never used one of them, always taking the one he was shaving with.
I'd seen him replace a used blade. Twisting the handle butterfly doors opened and the tiny strip of steel raised its self towards me. Sometimes there were tiny spots of rust along the edge where the razor had rested in wetness on the windowsill.
When finished I washed it and put it back.
A bathroom would remain my preferred place to cut.
There is no explanation for self-harm.
I cannot think of or tell a real reason for the cutting.

It stings, it hurts, and it degrades.

Was it about controlling the hurt?

I don't even think that is the answer.

And so I left.

I caught a bus to Dublin one Friday evening and waited outside a night club for a former school friend who had said I could stay with him over the weekend.

He had said he would help me find somewhere of my own to live. I left my bags at the bus station and would collect them the following morning.

Wasn't sure of where he lived, so we had arranged the previous weekend when he had been at home that we would meet on the steps outside a Nightclub in town.

I hoped he remembered.

I walked up and down the steps. Standing out on the pavement, watching people approach and walk on or pass by me into the club.

What if he didn't come?

I didn't have a plan B.

I didn't want to appear anxious and so moved my head and body to a silent tune that only I could hear.

After some time a doorman came over saying I couldn't stay there. I told him I was waiting for someone but he didn't believe me.

"This isn't the place. Move on round the corner."

As we talked my friend arrived, they knew each other as he used the club often.

The doorman laughed and said he thought I was a prostitute.

He apologised and we left.

We got very drunk and I had consensual sex for the first time.

The following afternoon I moved into a bed sit and became the person I wanted to be. I created myself in that small room.

I was Home.

There was no one to sneer or be compared with.

In my mind I built a past, family and home life that had never been.

Here she had no significance and I chose to bury what had happened.

It surfaced unexpectedly sometimes, something triggering an image and I would go to the bathroom. Throwing the blade away unsure when I would want one again.

I would stay behind my door until the feelings passed.

I rarely went home, unless for Christmas and other random dates and it made it easier to build.

Occasionally I met and dated the friend from school.

* * *

I lived on my own in the bed sit.

I was never afraid of being alone, darkness or strangers.

This alone was perfect and mine to fill.

Covered the walls with words from songs, quotes from books, movie posters, handbills advertising bands and comedians. Snippets from the newspapers, silly headlines and cartoons. Neatly stacked in a cupboard in one of the empty bed sits were magazines. The former resident had a subscription to Time and still the magazines fell through the letter box.

Black and white images of war, victims, protestors on their knees, politicians, the space race and global disasters overlapped with the frivolous.

I loved the cinema but my passion was reading.

Lack of money brought most to second hand books but they were my first choice.

I loved the feel of the used books

A smell unlike any other paper.

They had a story of their own, confirmed by finding another person's book mark.

I liked to believe they had a significance other than being something conveniently close to hand to hold a page. A playing card, sweet wrapper, a ticket to redeem photographs, a name and phone number. I loved books that were inscribed as presents, especially if they also bore a date.

There were a number of second hand book shops in the area where I lived. Shelves from floor to ceiling of horror, Sci-fi, romance and classic fiction. Slightly tattered books were stacked in heaps and traded for new.

I never bought books that were violated with turned down pages or broken spines. Feeling the last person who had read them hadn't cared when they had left down the volume flat at a bedside or on a table.

 Ten pages from the middle of my copy of The Day of The Jackal were missing and I had to get out of bed, walk into town to a book store, find a copy and read the missing text, returned to the bed and my creased pages.

I never traded my books in but stacked them and lined them along the skirting boards. My favourite kept close to the bed, so I could read the titles and try to remember the stories.

The house was old, in a state of disrepair, nearly all of its rooms unoccupied. The rent was low and once a month I got money towards it from the Rent Allowance Office.

Downstairs a girl from Limerick, Breda, who would be my friend and the only person I ever told about my childhood.

She would be the first person to take me to a hospital.

We had met in a night club in town, sharing the same table with people who knew each other. Her sister shared a house with four other girls and Breda slept on a mattress on the bedroom floor.

Breda had come Dublin to do a college course but had dropped out after a month unsure what she wanted.

Within two years her life would go wrong and we would lose each other.

A middle aged man, Liam, who we rarely saw, lived in the slightly bigger room next to mine.

He was the only other tenant of the house.

He left early each morning and returned to his home down the country every Friday. Coming back to the city on a Sunday night. The locks were broken on the doors to the empty rooms and sometimes we let friends stay in them. He didn't object. Never complained or knocked on the wall for us to be quiet when we played music or stayed up late running from one room to another in drunken games.

He left for work at the same time each morning.

The only times he would knock on the door was to say there was hot water.

I think he put extra money into the meter so we could wash.

And when there was a phone call.

A pay phone hung on the wall at the bottom of the stairs and some-one who passed through our lives taught us how to avoid paying for calls by tapping out the numbers in counted sequences. It wasn't that easy and a mistake meant starting again.

Liam made one call on a Wednesday evening.

No one ever rang him.

A friend of Breda's near the end of our time broke open the phone to get the few coins inside and the landlady had it disconnected.

Liam moved out around the same time.

He didn't say goodbye.

Breda and I signed on the dole and did cash-in-hand cleaning jobs.

Once a month we collected our rent allowances and spent the rest of the day in the cinema. Paying for the first film and then hiding in the toilets or standing at the concession counter to go to another screening of whatever was on the bill.

There were enough cinemas in Dublin city at the time to allow us to not have to return to the same one for months.

We watched everything.

Blockbuster, low budget, subtitled foreign language, animation and x rated soft porn.

There was a cinema along the Quays that we had never ventured into as it was known

for its seediness. My friend from school had told me that he and his housemates had gone there and that we should go just to see it.

The cinema stood out in a row of closed shops and empty doorways. It was one of the few places where people, men and women stood around. It was in an area close to the docks and early house pubs. There was a smell of decay, neglect and the unwanted. One film played throughout the day, the starting times listed from early until late.

We bought our tickets from a woman with a smile and walked through a heavy dusty fragrant curtain and down a darkened corri-dor.

We joked that it was like entering an adult ghost train.

The film playing was about a teenage prostitute and didn't pretend to be anything other than what it was. Cheaply filmed, low end with spotted faced actors.

The camera angles and scenes portrayed exactly what the viewer wanted.

The cinema was in an odd gloom that I've never been in since.

It turned the few people that were there into peculiarly lit dark shadows. We could hear them and see their outlines.

Pushing each other and giggling we sat into an empty row.

I could hear movement from behind me and a man was climbing across seats. His dark shape slid down into the seat next to mine.

Breda and I moved a little closer to each other.

I could hear him breathing and I knew that he wasn't watching the screen.

Could sense him looking at the side of my head.

I turned and he smiled.

He was masturbating.

I nudged Breda to look, she screamed and he continued.

We left our seats and ran, in the darkened room missing the Exit and running into a carpeted back wall.

We didn't try to keep quiet, shouting **"How do we get out?"**

We were answered with shouts and laughter.

A door opened and the woman who had sold us the tickets told us to leave.

We ran, laughing and for weeks after claimed we saw the man in all sorts of places, the more officious the better.

On days that we weren't working or going to the cinema we lay in either her or my bed, reading, talking, and planning. On nights when the empty rooms were dark and quiet we stayed in the house content to do nothing.

Sometimes I arranged to meet my old school friend but at the start neither Breda nor I dated anyone regularly and so most of our time was together.

Breda's room was downstairs at the front of the house, behind her bed a large bay window. We would lie on our stomachs, pillows under our chins, no head board blocking our view and watch people pass by.

Spotting regulars and giving them names, much like I would repeat years later locked inside a mental institution.

We knew who lived where and at what time they should return home. Next door a mother and two sons, both a lot older than us. One of them rode a motorbike and knocked on the door once in his leathers. He said they were having a party and apologised in advance for the noise. We both smiled at him but weren't invited.

His brother left out the bins in shorts and jogged morning and evening.

Across the road from us was an old folk's home, red brick walls met at gates and graveled paths twisted under trees and through an expanse of lawn.

Few of the residents sat in the garden or came out.

One winter's day we watched an old lady as she danced in the snow.

Her arms outstretched as she welcomed the falling flakes.

Her body moving with sheer joy and agelessness.

Her feet and mind at that moment wherever she believed them to be.

Watching her movements I was content that I knew what madness was.

We noticed the same woman most days pace outside the gate, a few steps in either direction but never leaving the pavement.

A bag clutched with both hands and held out in front of her away from her body.

Holding the bag seemed unnatural, as though it wasn't hers and she was keeping it safe for someone else. Gripping it tightly and in full view should whoever owned it return and reclaim it. Her head moving as though trying to find someone she had lost sight of in a crowd. She'd stay for hours until a staff member came outside and brought her back into the building.

One day she crossed the road, leaned across the wall outside our window and cried, her body draped like a discarded coat.

We laughed until it was no longer funny and Breda got up and went to see if the woman was alright.

She said she was waiting for her mother. That she had her bag, that her mother would be so happy and proud of her when she saw she hadn't lost it.

She didn't seem as funny anymore and we tried to ignore her.

We both secretly hoped she would die soon.

We began to pull the curtains in the afternoon.

I met the two strangers on Harold's Cross Bridge at six o'clock one evening. I was never afraid of strangers or frightened of what they could do, part of me didn't care and the other part didn't believe anything could happen to me.

I had no fear of sex or anything surrounding it, there was no novelty in a stranger's behaviour.

Breda had a found a part time job and so when on my own I did things she had no interest in.

Mainly exercise.

I had met the pair earlier in the day in the swimming baths. One of them had lost the key to his locker and I had retrieved it from the bottom of the pool.

Neither of them could swim but the pool was half price to the un-employed two afternoons mid-week and it passed their time.

Mine also.

For some reason, that I have no excuse for, or recollection of how it was discussed, it was decided that these two unknown boys would give me a tattoo.

Their qualifications for this task displayed in D.I.Y attempts on their arms and the face of one.

They were both tall and unhealthy looking and despite being in their early twenties looked like pubescent teenage boys. One of them had an animated smile that framed gapped straight white teeth.

The other had chewed fingernails with dots tattooed on his knuckles, and in a random spatter on his left cheek. He wore a silver identity bracelet with a girl's name on it.

He said it belonged to his sister.

They arrived on time and we went to a piece of waste ground that was hidden from view behind advertising hoardings. Facing us huge letters sprayed in different colours on the red brick of the flats that backed onto the abandoned space.

I could hear traffic noise on the busy road that ran alongside the canal and smell fumes from the buses as they stopped further along. Both boys lived nearby and said they were meeting friends in the pub on the other side of the bridge when we were finished. They asked me to go with them and I said I would.

The one with the bracelet had a small bottle of Indian ink and a pin. We had no pen or way of marking my arm, so a piece of coarse grass was chewed and used as a brush.

"Sorry if it hurts." He began to tap the pin into my skin.

The pub was small and dirty, the windows high up in the walls near the ceiling. They didn't seem to open and the amount of daylight let in was insufficient and unheeded.

The room was full, the crowd all standing.

There didn't appear to be any bar stools or seats.

There was no music, or television, but the room was loud with talk and laughter.

There was something underlying it and unpleasant in the sound.

The air actually felt like it was capable of meanness.

Each of the artists bought me drink. I had told them before we had got there that I had no money and they said it didn't matter. Others began to join us, to hand me pints and stand closer to me. All of the men were older than but knew the two I had arrived with.

I thought I was enjoying myself.

Getting drunk, allowing the men to put their arms around me, draw me closer to nuzzle my face, to leave their damp breath on my neck.

The boy with the smile said I really should go home, but not to say anything.

Leave as though going to the toilet.

As drunk and careless as I was I knew by him that I should leave. Outside he joined me and walked with me along the path, saying I shouldn't be as trusting as most people expect something in return.

"What do you expect?" Knowing I would willingly have consented to anything he asked.

"Nothing." Telling me that he wouldn't like to see anything happen to me and that they shouldn't have brought me to the bar.

He told me to look after myself and headed back to his friends.

Breda and I would meet him by chance sometime later and go with him to a party in a house without electricity and boarded up windows. There was no furniture and the awful smell came from the house and the people in it.

I left but Breda stayed and slept with him on a dirty mattress.

He was a drug addict by now and she said he cried in his sleep.

I had allowed strangers to daub Christianity's most recognisable symbol on my arm along with my initials. At first I was proud of my body art but became tired of explaining that it was a cross and not an X. As time passed it became something else I didn't wish to be reminded of and kept my sleeve tugged down to cover the never fading blue. When I catch a glimpse of it now in the mirror I hope my daughter has more common sense and self-worth.

Eleven

Today

I haven't heard Voices since getting here and hope they haven't forgotten me.

Today I share my days with people who understand wanting to die.

I don't mean the staff or visiting counsellors.

With Maria, Jackie or any of the others there is no shame or need to explain.

They know that what I did.

Tried.

Failed, didn't depose my loved ones.

Their fucked up minds see clearer than any trained clinician can ever hope to glimpse.

Jackie says I am at the starting point of tired sequence.

"They watch you.

Then.

They stop.

Like they're bored or have no answers."

I am allowed to walk to the smoking room on my own, the nurse lingers at the door of the office to make sure I have gone inside.

When I am finished I come back and wait for her.

I must tell them if I want to go to the toilet as I still have to be accompanied.

In the line of windows of the smoking room there is a door that leads out onto a balcony that is enclosed in mesh.

It resembles an aviary.

A balcony that someone thought a good idea. A nice treat for the original patrons is now regarded as a very bad tenet.

A balcony for people with self-harm issues that offers a decent drop ticks all the wrong boxes.

I've never seen anyone out on it and the door is bolted and pad-locked.

Reinforced insecurity for us to view the world and it to perceive us.

The corresponding doors on the men's ground floor ward are left open most days and I see patients who are free to wander in and out. Their smells and sounds pass steadily through.

I like this room but the noise from the smoke extractor is hard to ignore, once I allow myself to become aware of its hum it is hard to remain.

A little like lying in bed waiting for the next snore or unexplained noise.

There becomes a need to pre-empt the sound with a nod of intro-duction or acknowledgement.

An older woman who doesn't smoke but sits in here, jokes that the extractor is a device dreamt up by some sadistic doctor who controls and intensifies the pitch to bait us into irrational exchanges with each other.

"Probably writing a paper. Behaviour in our Mental Institu-tions."

Sometimes the noise is almost painful and only made bearable by our need to be here and to hear the sound of real voices.

This room is a strange place and seemingly not governed by any protocol anywhere else on the floor.

Downstairs harbours its identical male twin.

Their murmurs, sounds and smells penetrate from beneath our feet.

Words stream up and merge in a second hand marriage of echoes and drifting smoke.

Is there a male equivalent of each of us?

A psychotic Ying and Yang.

Because there is no where we can go the staff only peek at us through the glass of the doors. We are right next to their office and from their vantage point they can see who passes through the doors. Because of perceived governance of lack of restriction in this room each new day can determine the rules and the underdog.

One-Nighters are left to sit alone and avoided even with eye contact. They have no value as confidant or ally.

In this room we talk to each other, words shared and exchanged if only to ask for a light or a cigarette, that is promised to be replaced once the shop downstairs opens or a visitor comes.

Non-smokers will brave the foul smelling air we expel just for the activity that pervades.

Everything here must be kept within touching distance, held tight or develop the appropriate reflexes to protect your belongings. You soon become aware of who to share cigarettes with and who in turn won't see you stuck without a smoke.

More importantly who to hide them from.

Cigarettes become prey and the prize of angry outbursts.

The recently fallen are easily detected by leaving their cigarettes, sweets, or goodies out openly on display.

We all had to learn and no one tips you off and neither in turn did I.

I've seen Margaret snatch a bottle of coke and immediately spit into it so that it will become hers.

There are no words of abuse or threats she hasn't heard. She has been physically attacked and hurt, but it doesn't deter her.

I can't decide if it is an uncontrollable compulsion or just a clever game of interaction. Like an errant child who's misbehaviour demands attention and gains reward with reaction.

She will eat a cigarette if challenged to return what she has taken. She has her own but they are rationed by staff. An arrangement agreed upon with her children who bring her cigarettes every few days. They know that if the regime of rationing wasn't enforced she would smoke all they had brought in one marathon nicotine fest. Lighting up and smoking more than one at a time.

It has been decided that she is given one every half hour throughout the day. The last at 9pm, and first at 8.30am. For the privilege of each of these smokes she must go to the office, and wait for one of the staff to acknowledge her.

She is not supposed to knock.

When I first arrived here she was banging on the office door wailing words I couldn't make out. They are now familiar and I no longer hear them.

My husband and I had been courteously shown into a small room to wait for someone to admit me.

He held me and I cried as I listened to Margaret.

I begged him to please not leave me here.

Sitting there I wondered what grade of Hell I had traded up to.

He said it was for the best that I had to change, had to get better.

I now know that Margaret wasn't portentous and when she stands in front of me.

"Give me." I gladly give her the cigarette I am smoking.

Once in a while I will light a full one and give it to her, but she can become a nuisance if this is done too often.

I am not the only one who does it, but sometimes this simple act can be used by others to their advantage.

Bad people step forward everywhere.

If Catherine hasn't been able to get her way over deciding what television channel we watch, or just because she can, she will head to a nurse and tell that Margaret has been given a cigarette.

She is clever enough not to name anyone for the offence, for somewhere inside her there is also fear and she is wise not to take an unnecessary step-too-far.

Margaret loses one of her arranged smokes if caught.

Someone said Catherine is serving an indefinite prison sentence but I am not sure.

A favoured speech of hers is that she is different from us and that only trickery and unfortunate circumstance brought her here.

Sometimes, just for aversion, I challenge her.

She was chastising Maria for watching re-runs of a program. I was sitting against the wall trying to talk myself into some form of belief, not in the viewing area and ready to leave the room.

I overheard Catherine. **"Comedy for the masses!"**

She was sneering, standing in front of and lecturing Maria on the program she was watching. Accusing her of being unable to think for herself. Of not having a big enough brain to hold a view point or opinion of her own.

I moved over to the vacant chair directly in front of the television, my heart pounding with rage and fear, leaned forward and turned the volume up.

Said I wanted to watch it and she reached for the remote control.

I snatched it.

Our paths and hands crossed.

She screamed, called me vile names.

Most of the other woman quickly stubbed out their cigarettes and left the room muttering for Catherine to just go away. Those that stayed sat back, the promise of tension and conflict presented to them.

Catherine became quiet and sat down one side of me, Maria the other.

As each ended I asked Maria what she wanted to watch, confirming with the rest of the room the choice that was made.

I wanted desperately to cry.

Catherine whispered to me that she would remember my face, and that she didn't live that far from me outside of the safety of here.

I held Maria's hand tightly for reassurance.

Was I doing it for Maria or myself?

Somewhere deep inside a voice screamed against all that had happened in the years to lead to this room.

* * *

From the comfort of nicotine and tobacco fumes we watch non-smokers through a glass partition. They sit in silence in clothes that smell of fabric conditioner and the bodies within.

There is no idle, angry or wasted chat.

They all follow the Soaps and agree on which News and weather forecasts are best. They compromise and allow for someone who is following a Series.

They ask, **"Are you watching that?"** Before any button on the remote feels the pressure of a finger.
Catherine preys on them too.

When she has caused enough upset in here or can't get a reaction
or anyone to engage with her, she'll leave with a parting shot about
the disgusting smell of cigarettes and the class of people who
smoke.
She enters the clean leisure space with smiles and comments about
those she has left on the other side of the glass.
The residents of the room know that what is about to happen is un-
predictable. Sometimes Catherine sits and amicably watches their
television choices.
Mannerly and peacefully passing the time with them.
Flick of a mental coin and the passage of the evening veers into
uncertainty.
She'll shift furniture and drag tables across the floor, over and
back.
Rearranging the chairs, then sitting on them like an arch Goldilocks,
adding cushions, then throwing them aside.
Drawing the curtains.
Switching on and off the lights.
They rarely react with the same venom as she ignites within the
smokers and they generally ignore her. Prepared to wait it out and
for them this mostly works as she soon gives up and sits quietly to
watch their preferred entertainment.
Jackie says nonsmokers must not be as highly strung, are better
suited to mental hospitals or are getting better tranquilisers than
the smokers.

One evening Catherine became the Ringmaster of her own two
ring circus, dancing and skipping bare-footed between the two
rooms.
Twirling headscarves and laughing.
She concluded the First Act of her show by treating us all to a strip
tease after which she paraded naked through the rooms.
She vanished up the corridor to cheers and shouts.

Two nurses joined us and laughed when Catherine came back.

She returned with a bow after rummaging through the dirty laundry bags.

Dressed in whatever she could find, arms spread open like a Broadway star.

"Guess who?"

There was an odd form of pride displayed by those she mimicked and briefly a glimmer of fun and not her trademark nastiness in the performance.

Catherine's coin spun once more and what we were treated to was closer to what we expected.

She pulled down her trousers to reveal the soiled underwear she was modelling.

It belonged to a smoking room regular who stopped laughing and grabbed Catherine demanding she take them off. Catherine suddenly became shy of showing her flesh, refused to disrobe and held tightly to the purloined garments.

She became violent, letting go of the clothes, closing her fist and punching the woman full force into the face.

Both of the nurses hit the red buttons clipped to their identity passes and immediately

other members of staff ran into the room.

The women were separated, the owner of the clothes comforted and taken to the kitchen for tea.

Catherine managing to kick the trousers and underwear off as she was taken away.

We could hear her laughter getting fainter as she left the floor.

Smokers or non-smokers, we all share the same restlessness.

We all fidget and wait for days and time to pass.

Twelve

In those two brief years I became closer to Breda than I would ever be with anyone, male or female throughout my life.

Beside her bed was a photograph in a cardboard frame.

Along the top her name was spelt out.

Five felt letters each a different colour.

Said it was the first thing she had made when she started school. Was so proud of it and it always held a picture of something that was precious to her. There had been a dog, her grandmother, her and her brother in Halloween costumes, Duran Duran and now, a photograph of her much younger self.

She positioned the picture so it faced her opening eyes and it was the last thing she looked upon before sleep. I had seen her many times lift it, her fingertips linger on the image, silently communicating something across time.

In the photograph she was 15 years old, her hair shorter and dyed a bright orange.

Her face appeared puffy and bloated.

Lit by the light of a winter afternoon sitting on stone steps and smiling.

Although she was wrapped up with a scarf and coat a school uniform was discernable.

On the night I asked her she told me she was pregnant when it was taken, that no one knew.

Just her and her unborn child.

She said nothing of a father.

Days after the picture was taken she told her mother.

Said there had been shouting, tears and silence in her home. A local nurse, a family friend was consulted and through her it was decided it would be better for Breda to give up her child.

An adoption agency was contacted and her baby was born two months later.

No one thought to take a photograph of her daughter and the picture taken by a friend that lunchtime was all she had of the two of them together.

On that same night I told her about my sister, about what she created and directed between my brother and I.

"Is that why you cut?"

She held my arm and ran her fingers across scarred, raised, smooth skin.

I didn't tell her about the woman at karate.

I didn't tell because I knew that what the woman had done to me was vile and wrong, but that my memories with her were happy and that I craved her touch.

Upstairs I undressed and stood in the darkness recalling the woman's hand as it had closed over mine when I had put my finger tips to the strap of her bra.

She guided my hand over the material.

I could see the brownish colour of her nipples as they hardened and fought the bras restraint.

I cut my upper arms that night.

Didn't want Breda to see what I had done to myself.

I was ashamed of everything I had been made to do, everything that I had taken part in, and everything that I had taken a pleasure from.

Thirteen

Smoking at home became another secret.

My husband and whole family hate cigarettes.

In the dark I watched the glow of the clock and listened for his breathing to change. Sure that he was asleep I would roll onto my side and out onto the bedroom floor.

I'd remain there.

Motionless.

Waiting to be sure my movements hadn't disturbed him.

My cigarettes and lighter in a toiletries bag at the bottom of the laundry basket in the bathroom.

When Breda's relationship became serious, and dangerous, others stole from her. She joked no one ever thought to search through her dirty clothes.

I would go to the living room, open the window and climb out.

I was afraid to leave the house through a doorway for fear my husband or daughter would hear me.

Even if it was raining I'd climb through the opening.

Sheltering as tight as possible against the wall.

Virginia Creeper pushed into my back, spitting and tagging dead leaves and cob weds onto my shoulders, back and hair.

I would remain close to the slightly open window in case either of them called my name.

In the silence I talked all the time.

Whispering.

Some nights sitting outside, my quiet inner self bolstered with false bravery spoke and reasoned that I couldn't undo what had been done.

That I was a child.

So then.

As now.

Have no control over what she had done.

I stupidly believed that the memories and hurt would acquiesce and leave.

But they remained, ready and fueled.

Even now as a middle aged woman she has the power to dominate me.

Growing up and witnessing calendars hasn't stopped me from being the 8,9,11 or 16 year old.

She took control.

She knew we weren't going to tell.

Accusing her admitted our shame.

As things have unfolded I now know that it wouldn't have mattered if we had told.

Her true power dwelt in that knowledge.

Cigarettes finished I'd climb back in and push up the sash.

Rearranging anything that may have been moved on the sill or window board. Irrationally frantic as though with the coming of morning an inventory would be taken and my secret revealed.

On cold nights I'd lie close to the fireplace my face and hair in the ashes. Envying the exhaled blue grey smoke it's easy and complete release from its skin.

It was free to fall, rise, die or mix.

I scrubbed my hands to rid them of the clinging smell of tobacco.

Toothpaste brushed into my tongue, forcing the brush to the back of my throat until I gagged.

Swallowing mouthwash and changing my nightdress so nothing fingered my habit.

But still I didn't want to sleep.

Wanting to keep myself awake.

Trying to beat the night and the loneliness it heightened.

I'd empty the dishwasher, lifting the cups and plates one at a time. Placing them into cupboards with exaggerated care.

Sometimes I'd clean out the range, emptying the ashes into a lidded metal bucket inside the back hall. Lighting a fire so the kitchen would be warm and welcoming at breakfast.

With few hours of night remaining I would ease in alongside my husband, hoping that the sleep that was now demanding control would be dreamless.

Some nights he would be awake when I came back to bed.

I knew by the way he moved, but he never said anything or asked what I had been doing.

The night after the robbery I had been on my way down the stairs when I heard my daughter screaming. Her room across the landing from ours.

I stepped back up without turning and went to her.

She hadn't spoken.

She lay still and asleep.

I touched her hair.

From that moment every image and Voice collided and demanded full attention.

Bullied for it.

Reason began to dissolve and I started to leave the house at night.

To get into my car.

To drive, to find them, because they were coming back, back for what they really sought.

I made plans.

Bad things happen at night.

* * *

At night sound from unseen noises name those who are afraid.

Children know that no one is in control, and that uncertainty decides how to entertain the Darkness.

I went to her at night.

I wanted her to be scared.

Crying I held out my arms.

I had cut too deeply and the bleeding wouldn't stop.

The toilet paper I had wrapped around my arms drew colour to its surface and darkened.

I wanted her to make it stop, to ask why I had done it, to make the reason go away.

An open book lay beside her and they both slept on.

I could not hurt her.

I left the room praying they would not wake.

Never told her the games that were played when curtains blocked the daylight.

How it felt to hear whispered; "**let's play.**"

I stayed quiet and did not tell.

I bound my arms with cotton wading and plasters.

At night bathing them.

Some of the cuts became infected and a line of pus bubbled when I pushed my thumb along the scabs.

I had to be more careful.

Fourteen

Sometimes it is hard to keep track of how long I have been here.
I wonder how much the people at home know and just how much have I lost.
I know I will never be the same again.
What I have done will change how people react to me, their opinions already formed.
Those who think they know all the reasons behind my descent will never treat me the same and I have their uneasiness to take care of as well as my own.
How could they put me here?
That question won't go away, gnawing its way further inside.
My mind flicks like pages with a badly drawn cartoon figure in the right hand corners. Oh to be that simple figure, it can jump, walk or dance.
Lead a stationary or erratic quickened life.

Months before I came here I wrote to the address on a leaflet about abuse. I had brought it home from a hospital waiting room.
Twice the woman had written back.
She asked me to call her at the enclosed mobile phone number.
Said to ring if I found that easier than writing things down.
I'd purposely given no telephone number in case she called and either my daughter or husband answered.
She assured me that I didn't have to commit to or engage in anything that made me feel uncomfortable.

She finished her letter; *'but please make contact.'*
I didn't.
I hid her letters along with the leaflets and cigarettes.

My husband visited the other evening on his own, he does that sometimes.
To be honest I wish no one would come.
His phone rang and he stepped over to the window. I heard him talking, heard him say I was dealing with my little problem and would be back to normal in no time.
How could I argue with such blind faith?
When he left I was angry and hurt that he saw this as my little problem and that it would just magically go away.
An annoying bout of hiccups or heavy cold.
Sole ownership assured.
I don't really want to see anyone and I hate it when my parents come.
We sit in the smoking room, we don't say anything to each other and time hangs with no uttered words to pace its passage.
I watch their hands shaking and they avoid my eyes.
My father stands and we hug, and they walk away.
I have asked my husband to tell them not to come back.

Fifteen

On the day I prayed to die my mother was collecting my daughter from school. I had told her and my husband that I had a hospital appointment in the late afternoon. Ensuring I wouldn't be missed or expected home until late.

I had to go.

I wanted to take my daughter with me, but I couldn't be the one to end her young life.

What kind of sick God would re-untie us?

I thought the Lady from my childhood cared about me, but she tried to coax me to do wrong.

She had said how easy it would be to strap my daughter into the car.

They wouldn't question where I was taking her.

She trusted me to take care of her.

There was a straight stretch of road, I could gain speed and hit the wall.

I could kill us.

I knew that if I crashed the car and we remained alive, injured, I would never be allowed to hold or see her again.

I couldn't hurt her.

But I could protect her, with me gone she would never be alone and no one could get to her or harm her in anyway.

I had made my decision, was calm and ready.

I had a medical condition, a kidney complaint, that meant frequent Doctor and hospital visits. It also gave me access to a lot of medication.

I had been hoarding tablets that were categorised in the Medicines and Drugs Hand Book as; *overdose rating: High.*

Filled repeat prescriptions for painkillers and anti-coagulations and had been snacking on them for days waiting for something to tip.

I had no plan of where I was going when I left home.

A random turn of the steering wheel directed me to a wooded area at a lake not that far from my house.

I parked in the amenities area. There were a few people about but it wasn't the time of year for many visitors other than fishermen.

In a small car a middle aged man sat in the passenger seat, a teenage girl at the wheel. They laughed when she stalled the car.

The water was calm behind them.

I'd swam in the lake as a child and at fifteen had met two older boys one Sunday afternoon close by with a friend.

She'd met her beau the night before at a disco and arranged a meeting for the following day but didn't want to go alone.

It was too far to walk, too un-cool to cycle and so we'd hitched a lift not telling our parents or anyone where we were going.

A car pulled up and with the engine still running two boys got out. The car spun its wheels and the driver blew the horn.

Those inside cheered encouragement.

He had also brought a friend.

I stood in silence with a boy I instantly disliked whilst she disappeared beneath the trees with her date. The boy much like myself did not want to be there and had been cajoled into it with the promise of me. He motioned in the direction of the trees with his head implying we should do as our departed friends, who were now out of sight, and I thought maybe I should try a little harder and followed him. Crossing a footbridge into the trees.

Next to a tree we stopped and he spoke for the first time and asked me my name.

I don't think he heard or waited for my reply before pressing his lips against mine and laying his palm on my chest. I swore at him and he told me I was frigid and left shouting **"fuck you."**

I thought he'd come back, but he didn't and I wandered along another path that brought me to the foot bridge.

I remained for hours, ignoring families with running and cycling children and people out walking dogs that sniffed around my feet. These people all seemed to assume because we were out in the open bathed in the fresh air and sunlight of a relaxed weekend day, that it was taken for granted I would be pleasant. Each spoke or nodded a greeting. I would mumble a reply and if any made a return trip over the bridge I ignored them, turning and hanging over the railing of the bridge and spitting into the water below.

Sometime later my friend returned alone wearing a leather strap he had given her.

She showed it to me with pride saying it was called a Whang.

She thought she loved him.

The gift she said smelt of him and offered up her wrist for me to sniff.

It was like a chewed bootlace and smelt of sweat and teenage boy.

I was dismally envious of the souvenir.

I looked up the word Frigid when I went home, was unsure of the spelling and couldn't ask in case questioned as to why I wanted to know.

I eventually found it near the bottom a page, the second last word below Fright and above a wonderful word, Frijole, which I discovered was a Mexican bean.

I had to look up 'sexual impotent' and read a definition that mentioned sexually unresponsive to get its full meaning and I laughed.

I avoided the bridge and followed a track through regimentally grown Sitka Spruce. Quick growing commercial timber that matures straight, tall and fast.

None of it had been there on that Sunday afternoon when we met the boys.

I climbed a bank and pushed through briars to get amongst cover and out of sight.

There was a deep furrow, probably a trench created by the bucket of a digger when originally mounding this site for planting. It ran a

short distance before displaced earth collapsed back into the empti-
ness. Filled in overtime with ferns, nature's debris and new growth.
I lay down knowing I couldn't be seen by someone looking up
from the road or pathway.

No birds sang in the trees or moved amongst the sharp needles or
fine low colourless branches. but this was too much space to be
empty and it felt as though it was waiting to see what I wanted before it shared sounds or showed those that made their home or
traversed a thoroughfare in seclusion.

It's hard to judge time or grasp how quickly or slow it passes when
you have nothing that displays seconded movement. But I knew
evening was playing to a finish and
night baying to take its place.

I took my collection of tablets, a brand new blade for a Stanley
knife, cigarettes and a lighter from my pockets.

I had carried a bottle of water from the car and I began to swallow.
The light changed and sounds moved.

With the side of my face to the ground what I believed would be
my last night began.

I wanted no one to look for me and I didn't want to be found.

This was no cry for help, just a plea for permission to be excused.

I wasn't afraid.

I knew that whatever moved or dominated the shadows didn't
desire to hurt me.

My demons had never paraded beneath these trees and so received
no welcome.

Before I had left home I had ironed school uniforms, changed the
sheets on the beds. Fresh duvet covers with themed pillow cases.
Matched socks, cleaned the bathroom, fridge, and grease from the
top of the cooker and emptied the laundry basket of all it held.

I had to leave order.

Show them that I did care.

Strange reasoning that I was making it easier by leaving less of the
mundane things to be dealt with.

Somehow giving everyone more time to move on.

A permanent order and lasting structure.

Before I left I wrote **I love you** trailed by both of their names in coloured magnets on the fridge door.

I wonder did they see them.

I believed the letter in my pocket would explain and tell how hard every day had become. How I too had childhood fears that no one chased or caught.

That I was afraid.

I hear my sister and my voice in every child.

I listen to laughter and silence when other children come to play and anger myself that my mind questions the nature of their games.

I stand outside the door to listen to them and hate myself for questioning their friendship.

She is roughly the same age I was we when it began.

When my sister's actions meant our childhoods were ultimately forgotten.

I know all sorts of games.

Games with different rules.

I can play Murder in the Dark.

I can play it so well.

Be very still.

I won't make a giveaway sound.

Pick me.

I can keep secrets.

I said nothing in the letter about my fears for my daughter's life.

There was no need.

She was safe now.

Sixteen

A visit form the doctor this morning.
They don't see patients every day.
Like everything else in life it is a game.
They are busy shuffling time tables and attending clinics and Out Patient surgeries. Miles and hours of billed travelling to spend a few minutes with the anxious. For heads to nod and hear recycled and replicated advice. I am though grateful to the Free-Range-Mad as their needs make the days easier without having to show progress.
We can never be sure if the doctors will come and so each day after breakfast the waiting game is set in motion.
The nurses give no clue.
Like scouts we watch the car park from any available window.

There are three doctors so we know each car and registration number.
As a car approaches a sound like frenzied bingo callers spitting out numbers ripples throughout the unit. A full house is rare but all three have been known to cause panic and arrive together.
We freely give our opinions on who is best.
There is true relief when a main psychiatrist doesn't make a visit. Junior doctors are easier to fool and happy with either verbal or mute display.
Sometimes we can be unlucky and the whole entourage makes an unannounced afternoon call.

My doctor drives an old car with brand new tyres. There is a deep green colour beneath the dirt that coats it. His registration plate muddied and hard to discern. Through the back window it looks as though some one emptied a waste paper basket onto the back seat. His windscreen is fogged and you just know the seats are damp. That water leaks around one of the doors when the rain is heavy and prolonged.

Sitting in it has to be unpleasant.

When he pulls up he remains in the car and it's impossible to see what he does for the time that he sits there.

As though rehearsed two of his team appear at a passenger door.

They don't tap on the window or call out.

They stand not speaking to each other.

He then emerges in a pristine expensive suit and high shined shoes. His greying hair in curls that follow their own destiny. He carries a small brown briefcase under his arm.

It's handles broken and its appearance lets slip it has witnessed both of them age.

He never looks up towards the windows or betrays his interest with a glance.

He knows the game and how to play it.

A nurse comes for me and smiles as she brings me to the room used for these special mornings and in the afternoon this space is for group therapy and relaxation.

I hate these mornings, as I am again forced to play a part and pretend I am on the realisation of happiness.

I sit stranded as all around me they sit. Doctors of varying ranks of importance, nurses, therapists, public health visitor and the main man, head honcho, the professor of psychiatry at the sister teaching hospital. They are all fully armoured with note pads and individual files dedicated to me.

All with an opinion on what is best, best for me, *"moving forward"* their mantra.

I try not to look into their faces for most of the session and hope it will pass quickly as they happily discuss me. Everything they say could be done without me in the room but making me sit compounds how powerless I really am.

How my state of mind and future is theirs to decide.

I am merely a spectator without a flag or team to support.
A stray voice asks how I feel and have I thought of suicide?
I say I am fine and **"No, no suicidal thoughts."** Satisfied she enters my response into her file the truth irrelevant.
My lies seem to be what they want to hear and I wonder are they putting ticks next to the right answers on a check list, adding my scores on an index or just filling in blanks with noughts and crosses?
Apart from my family, and murder, suicide is all I think about.
The professor says he'd like to see me on his own when he has finished his rounds.
"Is that O.K?" I nod uncertainly and search his face for an answer.
I am dismissed with smiles and softly spoken words of encouragement.
On a chair outside the door the next patient waits to be called, we exchange a sort of semi-formed smile as I walk away.
I don't know how long it will be until I am called and so begin a slow drift along the hallway.
"Stay around here." A nurse says indicating with her hands where I am to remain. She stands with a file in her hand chatting to a doctor.
"I know." My answer not loud enough for her to hear.
Like a child I stand rocking slightly and swinging my arms.
I move just so she can't tell me what to do, fooling myself that I have a choice.
A few steps brings me as far as the water dispenser. I fill one of the small plastic cups and sip the always cool water.

During the summer my sister and her best friend would swim most days, rain or shine made no dent in their plans. They were both accomplished swimmers who had gained certificates for Survival and Safety. For two weeks each summer her friend went to stay with a maiden aunt who ran a post office in a small town in the North of Ireland. She would then bring me and although my brother and I endured her perverse cruelties I loved when we shared these kind of moments.

When we behaved like children and I pretended it hadn't happened or would now stop.

We'd pedal the four miles to the lake. Some days we'd speed through the journey, others it would take longer as we'd detour. Stopping, talking, and weaving from side-to-side on the road. Imitating how we imagined a frog, other animals, school friends or older relations and neighbours would ride a bike. We'd laugh loudly and sing versions of the latest songs.

The lake would teasingly come into sight and we'd cycle faster. Losing sight of it for a few moments as we free wheeled down a steep hill, legs held high and away from the spinning pedals.

Over a stone bridge and we would be there.

Early in the day, for most of the summer this place was theirs and now I was sharing it. We went to their spot, emptying our bags and arranging towels on the ground if the bank was dry. We always wore swimming costumes beneath our clothes. Undressed we'd disappear into the darkness that surrounded the lake, this was their ritual and I loved that she continued it with me.

It was dark, so dark in there. The time of day didn't matter as sunlight only trespassed where the trees allowed. The ground was soft and if I remained in one spot for any length of time, dark, boggy smelling water surrounded my feet.

My sister and her friend believed they had discovered the spring well that was hidden amongst the trees, although the large flat stones at its edge and sometimes an empty creamery can or water containers told of unseen others.

There was always a crisp clear coldness around it. It touched your skin like a sunny morning in winter. Kneeling down on the cold stones we'd cup our hands into the freezing water trying to get it to our mouths before the water ran through our fingers.

She'd plunge her head down and come up screaming. Shivering the drops flying everywhere and hitting my body.

She'd always coax me to do it, not in her usual mean way but I never got beyond dipping the top of my head into its harsh coldness.

I would be angry that I had disappointed her and promised I would do it one day.

"Leave yourself too much time to think." She'd say getting up. Water falling from her face and hair. Rivulets finding a path across her skin, a tremor of coldness itching her flesh.

Almost to prove myself I would run from under the trees and into the lake. No matter of how cold it first seemed I'd force myself down. The water pounding shock from my knees to my chest. Breathing hard I'd call out to her how lovely it was. She'd creep from the trees, tip-toeing to the water's edge. Entering the water, stopping every few steps, pulling her stomach in as the water rose up her body. She'd lift her arms higher letting her breath out in loud gasps.

"Get your shoulders down." My teeth chattering. Proud that I took the lead at this. Then she was down and that scream again.

In the hallway, I read the instructions of what to do in the event of a fire and counted the number of times the letter **a** is used on the notice pinned to a door telling of the times and days the hairdresser is available.

"He'll see you now." The same nurse leading me to the small consulting room I had
entered that first night.

The mood paint on the walls can't disguise the room or the enclosed and lost feelings it omits.

Somehow the room signifies the purpose of the whole building and makes me uncomfortable.

He asks me if I mind if a younger doctor sits in as she'll be around more frequently than him if I need someone to talk to.

I say it's fine.

I will readily agree to anything if I think it is in my favour or will make this meeting pass quicker.

She's younger than me, her skin appears as though it has never felt sunlight, a breeze or disappointment.

Ill looking my father-in-law would have called her.

She seems as maybe she could be imagined, assembled from images of unthreatening kindness sorted and stored in the pockets of my mind.

She seems nice, a snap assessment of a stranger.

We all guiltily judge books by covers.

I fidget, my hands to my mouth, my legs crossed and uncrossed.

"Is this bothering you?"

I tell him, but he is aware, that this is where I came on my first night and that I don't like being in it anymore now than then.

He looks around as though trying to see what scares me and stares back at me.

Says he is sorry but it was the only private space available to us.

"It is just a room.

Don't let it intimidate you."

It does.

He questions as to why the room makes me feel so anxious.

"I can't open the door."

"You will."

His colleague is all of the time writing, never looking up at me.

He has no use for silence and proceeds to tell me the reason why he needed to talk to me away from the others. My doctor has faxed him a letter, and my suicide note. He looks me directly in the face and says he can read from the note the things I haven't yet voiced to him since being here.

I lower my eyes, guilt and shame steal my reason.

I never thought I would have to deal with this.

It names her.

He names her.

In that awful room, for the first time since Breda, I say out loud for another person to hear and I cry.

He listens.

The young doctor writes.

Tears from deep within dirty with pain scorch my throat and lungs like running in frost. I have fought so hard to keep them at bay and now cannot stop their stampede. I've released a cat from a bag I never wished to hold.

C.S.A he calls it

"Childhood sexual abuse." The younger doctor mouths a whisper.

Silence regains control.

He says he wanted to talk to me alone away from the rest of the staff as he knows I harbour deep mistrust and despite what I feel about this place I am entitled to privacy. I have the right to choose to talk and who to talk to.

"None of what we talk about will be discussed with the nursing staff if you don't wish them to know."

Do I believe him?

I'd like to, but no, I don't.

He has arranged, with my approval for a counsellor to see me. He says through a smile that interestingly the counsellor realised I was the woman who had tried to make contact with her. She can meet me as early as tomorrow if I am happy to do so.

I know that at some stage to leave here I will have to give them answers other than my daily dispatch of **"I'm fine."**

Tells me that in order to reach any type of ending I will have to trust and agree to meet with someone to talk about what has brought me to this point.

I choose her as already I feel these people before me know too much and are no longer strangers. I am becoming guarded with what I want them to know.

I care how they will judge me.

He moves, allowing his body to assemble differently in the chair, a fresh topic a new position. He says there is another letter. One from my past that I sent to a friend, maybe twenty five or more years ago. It's not dated but she feels it would be that length of time since we were close.

He says her name, and for a moment I struggle to animate her. Then I know, a girl I sat with in school who hated everyone and had the same interests. I haven't seen her since finishing school all those years ago.

I laugh as I don't know what is in the letter. I have no idea of the contents. We always wrote to each other, notes and letters over school holidays as we lived in different towns. I can't remember all the raving and moaning we exchanged.

"It could be about anything."

I am certain it says nothing about my sister. During those years my shame and disgust were at their zenith and I was terrified someone would find out.

I say I am sure if I could retrieve something she had written a finger could be pointed and relevance attached to a future action.

"Where I am now sitting puts me at a disadvantage."

He agrees, thinks that the only person it should have been given to would be me as it was something private written and exchanged between friends.

He asks do I want it.

"No."

I don't want to see it.

Hold it.

Read it.

All it signifies is being let down by someone I once trusted.

"Throw it in a bin."

"I will."

The other doctor nods confirmation.

I bet everyone is coming up with snippets of conversations they had with me. Pinning importance to the recalled sound of my voice and how I moved my head or hands on any given day.

"I always knew there was something wrong with her, she chewed her lip when she wasn't speaking."

He tells me he doesn't have an easy answer and that my life is never going to be the same again.

That I will never be the same again.

What I have done will change how everyone reacts to me.

Those close who know the reason don't know how to treat me. May not believe me, and probably most, will think I should have left it in the past. That I should have accepted it, be glad it was over but leave it in the past.

I want to speak, to tell him I wish that I it only existed as memory, but it's here, it's today, and it's every day. That it determines how I behave and how I hide. That as I grow older the enormity of what she did and her betrayal of my love becomes more real. Moving on means that you leave something behind, but you can't when it is you.

Says he has to be honest with me, that I am going to be disappointed by many people. That for a time loneliness may even sound a little louder.

So much to look forward to.

"First step is to promise no step back."

I have to forgive myself for what wasn't my fault and come to terms and deal with the difficult truth that people you love let you down.

I tell him that is the hardest part of this, I used to believe that if those around me knew what was happening they'd protect me. But now I realise I was fooling myself.

Maybe somewhere within I didn't tell because I knew exactly how it would play out. Keeping waters calm beneath another's boat would always take precedence.

My value is my preparedness to settle for conditional love.

He smiles as he tells me there is light at the end of the tunnel and it's not an oncoming train.

I wonder how many times he has used that phrase and I wonder how much he is

actually listening to me and not just hearing another abused person.

"I know there are thoughts of suicide in your head. The air here isn't magic, so we won't fool each other pretending that your short time with us has cured all or any ills. So far all we have delivered is distance and separation from what haunts you.

You can give me all the right answers but it won't matter a damn till you give yourself the same ones.

Will you trust me?"

"Yes."

Are there choices?

"I'll take you off special watch and that way we are both placing our trust in each other."

He reaches forward and we shake hands to seal our covenant.

"Are you sure there is nothing else that you are not telling me?"

My heart pounds, can this man help me, can words defeat the hidden?

I shake my head, it feels less deceitful if I don't speak.

I can't tell him how I planned to murder.

I am now free to be alone, to wash, and take a shower.

I ask could I get a razor to shave my legs.

He laughs and gives me a look that displays an ordinary man.

He gathers his things, leaving the young doctor to explain to my nurse who has been waiting outside the door that I am now off special watch. As we walk away she says that I will begin to find things easier, and that she hopes it won't be long until I go home to my family.

At their mention I see my daughter when she began to stand in front of me and look straight into my face without saying a word.

Before she left the room her eyes lingering just a second longer.

The screams I heard were getting louder.

Did my daughter know?

I wonder should I go back and tell the doctor what I haven't told anyone, but it is unfinished.

I may still have to be deal with it.

* * *

I knew that my daughter was going to die.

I knew who would do it.

Their nick names, middle names and surnames.

Their faces and where they lived.

The cars they drove and brand of trainers they wore.

We live in a small Leitrim village and I know each of their parents since my own childhood.

I know what jobs they do, the shops they buy their groceries in, and the box they place their Xs into on Polling day.

But I don't know why their children chose my daughter.

I now know that they came to the house that night just to let me know how easy it was for them.

I was awake, reading and heard our dog barking.

Vicious. Unlike her.

I got up, thinking it had to be a cat or possibly a pine marten that had wandered too close. As I opened the front door the dog moved up the road in the darkness.

Kept barking and growling following whatever was annoying her.

I whistled and called her back but she would not come.

I could pinpoint the sound and knew she had stopped and was standing near the gate into the meadow on the corner.

The following morning a quad bike had been stolen from our yard.

Our lane is a dead end, our house the last one and a neighbour who lives below us has CCTV cameras. I told him the times I heard the dog barking and he played the tape for us and the two Garda who had taken our statements.

We all watched as two young men walked by unhurried.

They seemed to stand and face the camera, their faces unidentifiable with the yellow security light.

But I knew who they were.

They had spoken to my daughter as she walked by them outside the Chinese Takeaway the weekend before, saying her name and repeating it as she left.

They laughed as she got into the car.

I had asked her what they had said.

"I don't know." She shrugged.

As we drove away they waved.

On the television screen we watched them as they came back with the bike, one riding, and one running along behind.

The elder of the officers said they'd do their best and that we should not worry as the thieves had what they had come for and would not be back.

I wanted to tell them they were wrong but I remained silent.

My husband angrily told them that if they did he would shoot them.

The Garda laughed. **"Make sure and put a kitchen knife in the dead lad's hand before we arrive!"**

And that was it, they drove away, my husband went to work, my daughter to school and I nailed and screwed shut all the downstairs windows and the one in my daughter's bedroom.

That night, after I had checked on my daughter and returned to bed after smoking there was sounds of movement outside. Under my bedroom window I heard them shout **"Missus"**. I got up.
No sign of them.
I shook my husband awake and he said I was dreaming and maybe I should make an appointment to see a doctor to get something to calm me down.
But they were there, watching.
When I fell asleep terrible dreams unfolded. The dreams showed me what they intend to do. They made me sit and watch, her body resisting for as long as it could and they laughed as she died.
Daytime and wakefulness did not stop it.
I heard her scream my name, just my name.
That one word; **"Mammy!"** heaving with her terror, a plea for me to make it stop. Sometimes I would hear her voice from her room when I was totally alone in the house.
I'd stand still to be sure, and it was there, just a whisper that would replay and become hers **"what are you going to do?"**
The Brown Lady repeated the same question.
I left the house at night and drove. Sought them out, I knew they hung around outside the takeaway at night playing at being hard men and brave with younger. I made sure they saw me as I drove by. Slowing down and pulling my finger across my neck as though slicing through.
Pointing and smiling at them.
I no longer paid heed to the exaggerated motions of their tongues. The intent they displayed with their bodies or the obscene gestures as I knew their hands would soon be stilled.
I checked and rechecked the kill shots I wanted to make and read over and over;
'10 seconds to simultaneously suffocate and choke.
Sever the spinal cord in the neck.
Sever an artery or vein penetrating the heart or lungs.
Tightened all screws, bolts and sight screws.

Seventeen

It's getting late now. I hope my husband hasn't sent our daughter back to her own bedroom.

He promised she'd sleep in our room.

In our bedroom we have what we jokingly call **"the double, double single bed."**

It's the width of the room and comfortably fits the three of us.

Some nights when no one wants to sleep alone or stories are too scary or silly not to listen to we lie next to each other, and on these nights I don't leave my bed.

Lying in it **Badger** became a word that couldn't be said in our house without sniggering. A whimsy story my husband made up and added nonsense to about a woman neighbour. In the story she kept one of the animals as a pet and when she lost it he asked each of us in turn. **"Have you seen Maggie's badger?"**

At first we were silent then filled the room with dominoed laughter as for some reason **Maggie's Badger** took on a rude meaning. Much as when I first read **Chicken Balls** from a menu. Still the words elicit smiles and naughty laughter.

Thinking about her makes me smile and miss her more.

Smells kick moments and places to ambush me.

Earlier someone was chewing that awful pink gum she likes.

Sickly sweet synthetic aroma that I curse and scream **"Get away from me with that!"**

I looked around expecting, hoping to see her attempt to blow bubbles whilst a thick syrupy glue drips from her mouth. To hear her laugh when she sucks the mess back in across her lips and teeth. Then runs her hand across her chin and continues to chaw.

I wonder can they get my scent from a pillowcase or dressing gown.

Does anything evoke my essence?

The smoking room lights will soon be switched off and the door locked. A few more pulls before I mark the end of another day with cold water thrown on my face and toothpaste purging the taste of cigarettes from my mouth.

This is my last night of sleeping in a room on my own and I am no longer shadowed by a nurse.

"Not so special anymore." Jackie joked before she left for bed.

When the nurses come round with the nightly medications I for the first time refuse sleeping tablets. They both say I really should take them as they are aware that without them I don't sleep well.

"You are written up for them on request.

Get a good night's sleep." she urges.

I still refuse, the idea of being in a deep sleep frightens me as it's hard to get out of dreams.

I know my sister and my daughter's killers wait for me there.

When I took the anti-depressants they gave me in the first few days I dreamt of people I knew but with huge heads and distorted voices, the dreams the tablets fed were worse than my pre-packed ones. I had asked to be prescribed something different explaining what the pills provoked.

One of the nurses said she had heard of some others suffering the same side effects.

I have been prescribed something else but there is little difference in how they make me think or dream.

Asleep or awake they are always in my head.

The nurse pushes open the door with her foot and asks me to finish up as quickly as possible.

The door is locked for most of the night hours.

I guess mainly to make us sleep as the option of sitting here all night would surely entice many takers.

I stub out my cigarette, a strip of cellophane from a cigarette packet in the ashtray begins to char and smoulder. The smoke rises but the cellophane doesn't really burn, it melts and ceases to be.

Caught by the dark smoke and the faint smell I see my brother as he builds a bonfire. He would take ages arranging boxes as houses or blocks of flats, placing any plastic containers inside.

"So as to be realistic." He'd say.

"We need choking chemical smoke as the furniture."

One box would always be a warehouse filled with explosives so that people would die within. Screaming as flames took hold and making pitiful sounds of terrible agonising deaths as the boxes fluttered in charred pieces into the air.

He never allowed survivors and rescuers usually perished.

Sometimes he gave the victims' names.

Our sister had died in a building that collapsed.

He'd melt plastic to hear its scarring dribble. He had dripped some onto his hand and had to hide the burn. There is a faint scar only visible because I know it is there.

I think he burnt himself on purpose.

Finished we would sniff each other's clothes as we had been told when burning rubbish not to mess.

Alone I see this room as it is, big, ugly and stained.

Empty of all but me.

Night is the only time here that actually scares me.

Not the dimmed lights or darkened corners.

Something else that I can't describe, it seems to enforce what the place really is.

Pitiless.

At night it feels as though no one is in charge and different rules apply. The tormented sleep but still rave and the restless wander without leaving their beds.

Women who appear like wax for most of the day scream out loud once night descends and unsettles. Hidden somewhere throughout the day Malevolence appears. Sometimes at night I hear screams and shouts from the men's ward below us.

Their sounds called through the darkened air to arrive more menacing.

It's somehow easier to deal with this captivity during the day.

I no longer notice the girl who rocks from side-to-side.

I'm not alarmed when Edith comes out of the bathroom her face raw and maybe bleeding from scrubbing herself with a nail brush. Or the sight of Maria on days when she faces the wall on her knees and asks her god for forgiveness.

The night is long and I miss my child.

* * *

This morning I have become just another loony, not seen as an immediate threat to myself or any other's harm.

Not really special at all.

I will get my clothes back.

Being allowed to dress removes the scarlet letter pajamas and slippers denote.

The head nurse tells me they have to sort out a bed for me in one of the wards and to leave my things where they are until the paper work and practicalities are sorted out.

I am to call back to the office after breakfast.

Most of the others are already gone to the small dining room and this is my first morning not to be one of the first there waiting for the door to open.

Jackie points to vacant seats at the table her and Maria share.

She is smiling.

Nothing really changes in our lives. As young children on our first day in school we befriend someone because they smile, or share something they hold. At work we gravitate to the ones who smile and laugh at the same things. We socialise with likeminded people and hope to find a mate who will find humour and desire in the same moments. Even in mental hospitals we slot into a gang with the ones who smile at us and look around, judge and see the same things.

I sit next to Maria, Jackie across the table from me. She is already showered, her hair straightened, and full make up in place.

"Remember they are still watching you." Tiny specks of black mascara sit on her cheek.

Laughing her and Maria warn me to be on guard at all times.

"In the midst of a seemingly inane conversation a nurse will throw a random personnel question with the hope of having relaxed your tongue enough to hand over what they really want to hear.

"Who do you really think you are?

Have you tasted human flesh?

At what age did you first realise you were mad?"

"Or when did you last smoke a bit of Whack?" Maria shrugs.

After breakfast a nurse walked with me talking about books and our favourite authors. She enjoyed crime fiction and then without switching tone enquired had I ever made an attempt on my life before.

I glanced towards Maria who had heard.

She raised her finger to her lips in a keep-it-secret motion.

"No."

That was the truth. I had never tried to kill myself before. I had on occasion taken myself close. I learned which easily bought products caused me to become drowsy, a sensation I knew would fuse my dreams and let me drop and fall.

The cuts had been to satisfy other needs.

No cries for help or suicide attempts.

Breda had taken me to hospital the first time that I really hurt myself.

But if I hadn't fallen down the stairs there would have been no need.

Her sister was having a house party and Breda said for me to come along.

"Not spending the night with those boring shites."

She and I drank on our way to the house on the north side of the city.

We were very drunk and antagonistic by the time we got there.

The music was loud, the gathered house mates and friends were older than us with

nothing in common apart from alcohol and Breda's sister.

Someone asked Breda what she was doing with herself since leaving the house and college.

Breda laughed. **"As little as possible."**

There was then a conversation about how quickly she would realise she was wasting her life.

I left with Breda calling someone **"A pretentious arsehole!"**

"Where's the bathroom?"

"Top of the stairs."

A few people stood on the lower steps and I excused myself by them.

The toilet door was shut and there was a male and female sound trying not to be heard.

I knocked and they became silent.

"Wait a minute."

I noticed there was no one else upstairs and like Goldilocks went into each of the three rooms not knowing what I sought, but seeking out what was just right.

Next to the second bed were three bottles of tablets. Prescribed medication with Chemist labels. I had no idea what they were for, or whether they were antibiotics or pain relief. I tipped the pills into my hand then into my mouth washed down with the can I carried.

I took everything before me belonging to each of the tenants of the house.

Vitamin capsules and throat lozenges that I chewed as I moved around.

The toilet door opened and I heard whispered voices as they headed down stairs.

I saw a woman coming up the stairs and ran to get into the bathroom before her.

"Don't be long." She shouted.

A shelf held cough, and flu remedies and tablets that promised

relief from period cramps. The can was empty so I bent over the

sink and filled my mouth from the cold tap. Straighten up and the

mirror showed me a person I didn't much like.

"Will you hurry up I'm bursting!" She spoke to someone else

on the landing.

On the edge of the bath was a packet of disposable razors.

Alcohol caused me to sway, what I had swallowed hadn't had a chance to take effect.

"Are you near finished?!"

"In a minute."

I cut, whispering sounds.

"What are you at?" A new voice.

It sounded as though a few people were on the other side of the door.

I heard Breda, her voice against the door. **"Please come out... .shut up!"**

She was shouting at someone next to her.

I had left the lights on in the rooms and dropped the bottles wherever they fell.

I opened the door.

I hadn't thought about what would happen when I left that room. I never did when I self-harmed, there was never anything beyond that moment.

It was as if the party had moved onto the stairs. The lights were on and the music had stopped.

I dropped the bloodied piece of the razor and moved by the shouting woman who stood there.

"Aar what have you done?" Breda reached for me tugging down my sleeves.

The other party goers jostled to get me down the stairs.

I pushed through the angry faces and after a few steps I fell.

There was screaming and bodies and faces above me.

"No no, no." Breda pushed her way next to me.

"Ring an Ambulance."

"Get a taxi.... Please." Breda calmly spoke to her sister.

As she sat me up blood trickled from my hair and down the side of my face.

"I want to go home."

"Need to get that looked at first." She put her fingers into the blood.

"Get her out of here." Breda with the help of some others got me up and walked me outside into the front garden.

Eighteen

My belongings sit on a single bed. A freshly laundered duvet cover beneath them. It's a deep blue colour and I'm not sure if there is check in the design.

"Getting there." The smile from the young nurse standing next to me seems genuine and I don't feel ill at ease or embarrassed by where I am.

"Am I allowed to take a shower by myself now?"

She says yes, but she will have to open the door for me and that it can't be locked from the inside.

"If you push over what would have been the lock a card slips into the Occupied position so others know the shower is in use."

I am not allowed to stay longer than ten minutes and a nurse will probably be down to check on me during that time.

Even with the restrictions and fake privacy a shower without an overseer has me in a state of disproportionate joy and optimism.

I gather my shampoo, conditioner, soap and comb. I have picked out my clothes for the day, an out-fit, and sartorially special in track suit bottoms and a fleece.

As we walk to the shower room she tells me that I can now use the washing machine if I want to do my own laundry instead of sending it home. There is a list in the office if I want to put my name down. I think I'll pass.

This place is different today, off Special Watch suddenly I am a different person who can make mundane decisions with time diverting activities to plan for.

New rules.

New boundaries.

New things to remember and new ways to pass my days but still clearly within their markings.

In the bathroom I wonder when they begin their ten minute count, is it from the moment she unlocks the door or when she returns to the office?

Would I have enough time to kill myself?

The shower head is fixed to the wall, no hose.

There is no shower curtain, no dangling cords or objects to swallow. The ceiling is high and the recessed light bulb and electrocution out of reach. The water tepid, injury or scaring from scalding ruled out by the solitary temperature setting. I am sure that the truly inventive or quick witted could deliver death in this tiled space.

A knock on the door and my name sifts through.

I answer that I am getting dressed.

With my ten minutes used up and breakfast over a small portion of my day has been dismissed and I ask can I go outside.

"Not the first day, take your time." She seems aware of my frustration and tells me I am allowed downstairs to the shop but no further.

Outside I suppose is a privilege and I think tied up with how forthcoming I will be in today's counselling session.

When I trust they trust.

Tit for tat.

I have a small amount of money in my bag and don't care what I spend it on.

The shop is tiny, a few shelves and a counter built into a windowless recess. It is run by volunteers and sells two brands of cigarettes, pens, note pads, puzzle books, crisps, apples, stamps and envelopes. Toiletries and the like are not stocked. No aspirin or indigestion remedies.

The shop waits in the hall at the end of the men's section and I can see them move about. Their smells and sounds now closer, touching, pressing for recognition.

Next to the shop is the staff canteen and they sit and pretend not to be interested in what is going on during their break times but they watch, they remember.

Before I go back upstairs I stand and face the dusty panes of glass in the front door.

I can see outside.

I can see what I have been looking down upon from the windows above.

I promise myself I will be there soon.

The doors look heavy and hard to push open. The man at the reception desk smiles *hello* and I am glad of his kindness.

When I was a child a neighbour from home was a patient in the old hospital. When he left his family talked about him as though he had committed a crime.

We were told he had to go away.

Each Sunday a brother of his wife drove her to see him.

When he came home we were told not to annoy him but we were curious.

He had changed.

There was no humour anymore in his stories and he would ask us to leave.

Told my brother and me about a man he had met. An old man, a man who had lived all but seventeen years of his life in the hospital. Shortly after his father's death his mother had remarried and became pregnant. There was no place for him in the new arrangement.

She had him committed saying she feared for her and her unborn child's safety.

It was so easy, there was no one there to argue for him.

He had remained for what was left of his early adulthood, through his twenties, thirties and years beyond. His mother was dead, his half-sister had died in infancy and there was no one left who knew about him.

Each day for over twenty of his last years he sat in the entrance hall watching the door open and close.

Watching the people who passed through.

In and out.

Staff, visitors, the curious.

Sometimes he would step within an arm's reach of the handle, but never raised his fingers to touch.

Mostly he stayed and watched.

Invisible now, a permanent fixture.

One morning he was gone.

He walked out the door and kept going.

After some hours he came back saying there was nowhere he knew to go.

He climbed the stairs back to the ward and never went down to the hallway again.

He died in his sleep shortly afterwards.

* * *

I have switched off my phone.

I don't want to purposely ignore anyone.

Today has been hard.

After the triumph of going downstairs, when I went back to the ward there was a woman waiting to see me.

Again I was brought to that damn room.

She introduced herself.

I knew already who she was.

My counsellor.

She said she was glad to finally meet me and had thought of me many times since my approach and wondered what had become of me.

Expressed regret that events had brought me to this place before we got to meet face-to-face.

I think she is being honest.

Before we begin she tells me that she doesn't think she'll get to see me very often whilst I am still here as she has many other patients scheduled and a hefty waiting list. Will be working with me mostly when I leave, feels it's important that no matter how far into the future that may prove to be that I won't be meeting with a stranger when that time comes. Hopes that in that future to become more to me than just an appointment I am required to keep.

I tell her that I wasn't sure I wanted to meet her.

"It's natural to feel that way." I put my fingertips to my mouth and suck in a deep breath.

"We don't have to speak." Silenced roared to be filled.

Prompted or cajoled or genuinely willing, the loathsome words tumbled from my mouth. They fell undressed and indifferent to the damage their actions shaped.

During the session I said hidden words out loud, words I hadn't uttered since Breda. Told of hate, gave voice to recurring memories that have remained in the ascendancy in my thoughts.

How different they taste in confession.

I felt sick.

I asked her where our demons fly when released and had she ever hidden under a bed.

"As a fully grown woman pulled yourself in tight praying night will forget you?"

I need to be on my own.

PART II

One

My bed is on the left just inside the door against the wall.
It is a six bed ward.
I pull the curtain around my space whenever I spend time here.
To sleep, to read, to think, to be alone.
Two chairs mark my territory at the side of the bed.
I have a bedside locker and a small wardrobe that also contains three draws.
My case and shoes are pushed under the bed.
My slippers I leave above the covers at my side when I lie down.
The bed next to me is empty, so to the one the far side of the room facing it.
"Can I call you Kathleen?
I forget things."
I think Nan has been sent to me by some perverse deity.
Someone for me to watch over and not think solely of myself.
Despite what I now concede about myself, she doesn't belong here.

She is old and forgetful.
A privilege age should be allowed to bestow.
She is here for Assessment.
To see can she be left on her own for her remaining years.
To determine a capability of colouring within the lines.
They watch her as she bathes and ask how often she changes her underwear, and if she has had any embarrassing accidents. They

don't use sound when they question her about the intimate but mouth and patronisingly nod.

Continuously they question about her date of birth.

If she can remember her grandchildren's birth dates, their ages, names, her address and if she has had any surgical procedures.

Once the list of questions have been ran through they mark off the day and re-date their papers for the next.

She laughs. **"I don't think I'm one of the Spice Girls————I just forget things——I'm 81 for God's sake!"**

She tells me that at home she sometimes gets up in the middle of the night and cooks her dinner.

"That's all they're interested in."

Not that since her husband died two years ago she sleeps late and sometimes doesn't sleep at all.

"I live alone, who am I disturbing putting the pan on when it's dark outside?!"

"You'll set fire to the house Mother." She mimics.

"What harm is it to anyone when I eat?"

She waves across the room at me and laughs beneath the blankets at what she calls our wickedness for listening when Monica argues with the social worker and lectures her on bad behaviour and grammar. There's delight between us when Monica doesn't disappoint and daily dismisses the pompous woman with an eloquent.

"Fuck off!"

She prays for me and I try to protect her from those who abuse her kindness and take advantage of her always on offer sweets and biscuits.

Each night she asks me to call her when I wake and make sure she is on time for breakfast.

"Goodnight my Kathleen across the room and God Bless."

The light from the hall disturbs her and I pull the curtain around her bed so she can sleep.

Makes me promise to wake her if she talks in her sleep.

She does, but I let her dream on.

I still find it hard to sleep and try not to think about my daughter. Divert my ghosts with other memories.

"Like old clothes you never wear, have to get rid of them some-time." Jackie said one morning when filled with plans and tools to deal with her past.
"But you hang on to one or two even though they don't fit."

* * *

Breda was becoming more involved with the boy with the smile, his friends and ways. Although at the beginning I had sat and happily smoked and taken part in shoplifting truth or dare with them, I knew our lives were beginning an inevitable parting.
Our own stupidity, company and alcohol offered pale highs compared with what was now at her fingertips.
Liam had left and those that stayed in the empty rooms looked at home in the untidiness and mess.
The landlady came at the end of the week, collected the rent at the front door and had no interest in coming into the house.
I began to lock my door when I was in my room.
My relationship with the friend from school became more serious but he refused to come to the house and so we slept together only at his flat.

"Open the door. Open the fucking door" Even screaming I recognised the voice of the boy with the smile.
He was kicking my door.
"Come on!" Terror in his voice.
It was early evening, just getting dark.
I got up from my bed frightened by the panic in the sounds he made.
I slowly opened the door.
Through tears he told me to go to Breda.
Snot mixed and puddled on his top lip.
Their room was downstairs, the first doorway off the entrance hall.
The light of a bedside lamp shone out through the open doorway and I stood not wanting to go any further.
I could feel her lying there.
Crying.
The front door was open, the boy with the smile out on the road screaming for someone to call an ambulance.

I moved.

Towels lay on the floor.

Something bad had happened.

She jerked, twisted, trying to move. Pulling down the blankets, the sheets were soaked, a bloodied towel pushed up between her legs.

She shouted at me.

Begged me to get more.

The wardrobe door hung open.

I grabbed and pulled.

Sheets and towels fell to the floor and I scrambled to get as many as I could.

They touched my face, they were rough and smelt unused and old like dated newspapers that line a draw.

I dropped them next to the bed and stood there.

She kept reaching towards me.

I did not want her to touch me.

Inside my head I screamed; **"Please don't say my name."**

Forgive me, but all her helplessness, crying, pain and I wanted to run, to hide.

I was afraid she was going to tell me she was dying.

She began to whisper.

"Don't tell anyone."

"What have you done?"

I didn't want to share this.

I already had too many secrets to keep.

"I couldn't have a baby... not now." She cried, words and tears choking her, her body shaking uncontrollably.

"In here in here!" The boy with the smile came rushing in. Two paramedics along with him.

I stepped out into the hallway.

There seemed to be so much noise. I heard the back door open and slam shut as others left the dirty rooms and disappeared down the back lane way.

I was cold, still bare footed and wearing only a nightdress that now bore an odd pattern. The material beginning to dry and harden.

From where I stood I could see the flashing lights of an ambulance on the road. The people standing round it lit, talking and trying to see what was going on within the house. One of the brothers from next door was standing away from the rest a little further up the path.

He called me with his hand.

He had called the ambulance.

"Is she alright?" I told him the truth, I didn't know.

I stepped back into the house and the bedroom door opened, the boy with the smile carried her wrapped in a blanket. She appeared so small, and her bare feet swung and hit against his waist.

"You'll have to let us take her."

One paramedic ran in front and opened the back of the ambulance, the other at the Breda's side. The boy with the smile finally gave her up to them when they promised him he could travel along with her.

One of them came back.

He questioned me did I know what they had been using?

I had no idea.

"Do you know how many weeks she was?"

I hadn't known she was pregnant.

Had she.

They all drove away and I never said Goodbye to her.

Their room was empty now and night taunted and laughed at me.

I stripped the bed of what I did not really understand.

A darkened patch the mattress already screamed to keep.

I filled my arms and dropped what seemed like her shame into a plastic laundry basket. The cloth imprinted with her pain, my skin indelibly marked.

In a shed in the yard there was a twin tub washing machine we rarely used.

I filled the tub with water and set it to boil, then gathered the rest of the towels and bed linen from the floor.

There were no dry sheets to remake their bed and so I turned off the light and closed the door leaving the odd smell inside.

I went to my room.

How easy it would have been to climb back into my bed and leave the water boiling.

I don't know when I started to cry, I was so scared, my mind tripping over what it did not understand.

Why hadn't she told me?

What had they been doing?

The window shone with blackness and night was proving why we were frightened of it.

There were hours before morning and time for me to wash it all away.

As I dropped each towel into the water, soft, spongy lumps stuck to my fingers. They were parts of Breda, filled with her blood and pain. These odd sightless blobs had made her scream.

The water drained into the sink fleeing the pipe like an open vein. Threw more and more water in but still it spilled pink. I watched as it disappeared, getting rid of what had happened. I closed the lid of the spin dryer and the machine rattled and hopped on the concrete floor.

A hum filling the room.

Morning was near and I shook the towels as I hung them on the clothes line, still bits clung to them, now washed of their living colour. I flicked them off into the grass repulsed that they had touched me. They'd made her scream, and night was still laughing.

I fell asleep, and was woken by the front door swinging shut. I heard noises downstairs. The door to Breda's room was open. The boy with the smile and another girl were filling a bag with Breda's things.

He wouldn't answer my questions as to what had happened and where she was.

"She said go home." He left.

A mixture of half smoked and stubbed cigarettes and joints filled the ashtrays. Empty packets, papers, and clothing fought for the floor and I was totally alone in that house.

Fate and chance shake hands on deals they make with our lives. Choking on the conceited knowledge we have done what they brokered.

I wondered if I had never got the stupid tattoo would Breda and I have been happy in the world we had created.

I never brought the sheets or towels in off the line.

And.

I never saw her again.

Two

I asked Mary, the head nurse if I could go outside for a walk.
She thought it a great idea.
"But not too far." Pointed through the window to beyond where
the cameras watch. **"You'll need a coat."**
She told me to come and tell her when I was ready to go.
I now go every day and every chance I get.
I no longer have to ask for permission.
Through the glass of the office door eye contact grants approval.
On days when voices are raised and actions uncertain the ward
door remains locked and I have to ask to be let out.
"Enjoy your walk."
There is a distinct clicking as the lock is released.
Almost a sigh.
As I leave the door quickly swings back and automatically locks.
There is a buzzer on the wall to ring when I return.
A piece of card states for virgin entrants;
If DOOR IS LOCKED RING FOR ASSISTANCE
Released I head downstairs into the large entrance hall with its
highly polished wooden floor. I don't wait to register any sounds
and I nod good morning to whoever is seated behind the desk.
Neither the man nor woman who sit there ever ignore me. Always
so polite with or without words. Simple shrugs or just a smile.
I make sure to be seen smile back.
I am grateful for their acceptance.
Could they be former patients?

I stand before the door, a door that has power beyond pronouncement. Like well-practiced rituals each day in slow motion I hold the handle with care and pull. It secretes a sound of its very own and grants simple wishes of freedom.

It opens easily as though each day granting this snatch of Time as a favour.

I let go of the handle and step through the open doorway as the door begins its slow yawn to closure.

All the air from the keyhole has gathered and like a delighted puppy ready for play greets me. Flicking my hair and skin, demanding my immediate attention and recognition.

I stand for the intimacy of its touch.

Drawing it deep inside and upon my body.

I feel elated, this is my victory, and no one can run by, steal this time or claim a stake in my present.

I know that once outside the building they watch and monitor me from the office window but I don't care. I am now separate, my thoughts no longer tethered.

Left or right?

I now know it takes exactly nine minutes to walk at a careful non-rushed pace the circuit around the building and back to the raised step of the front entrance. I usually do three rounds each time I am out.

As I walk I talk to myself constantly, pitching bold, courageous retorts to accusations. Calmly speaking with reasoned voice.

Easy solitary bravado.

I ignore words and whispers that try to reach me through the air.

I wonder am I fooling myself by believing I don't belong here. I look at myself and I see I am dressed as any ordinary person and wonder would I be mistaken for a visitor or an employee, do I walk with the gait of the sane?

A high security fence encloses the boundaries with an opening at the front of the building for a small car park and footpath. Briars seep through the spaces in the fence and tendril out onto the path. They grip and invade any cracks or presented weakness.

At the back of the building beyond the fence cattle graze in the fields, audible their conquering sound as they rip and pull grass to their mouths.

All around me there are unwrapped senses.

The air smells fresh and unhurried.

A line of evergreen trees grow on the other side of the fence along the back. They smell like Christmas and are cut to the level of the fence. There is rubbish beneath them, things thrown from here and drink cans. Nearby a disenchanted condom makes me sad, as I feel somebody, just like it, has been used.

One woman said she had sex with a delivery man behind the bins that are near the steps leading into the kitchen.

Maybe.

I can see mountains and know the sea lies at their feet.

Like all good crazy people I am drawn to water and love the knowledge that no one can control the waves, how fast, slow or angry they move.

The lawns at the front are kept mown and raked of unruly wayward leaves.

A section of the lawn is cordoned off with a high wooden fence, forming an enclosed space along the side of the building. This is Special Care and sexual birth status is no significance to residency. On dry days I sit on one of the benches. The male wards provide the back drop sounds. Their French doors are often left open and they wander in and out.

Not caged like their upstairs silhouettes.

Mark joined me one day. He spits continuously and apologises for the filthy habit.

His body shakes like Parkinson's. The irreversible effects of prolonged use of drugs.

Both medically prescribed and self-approved.

That first day he told me he was mentally deranged. Diagnosed delusional as he had told a doctor that he was going to be President. Jokingly I advised him to say that he could be President and days later he told me that they said he was making progress.

We meet most days, unintentionally and usually only to say hello or acknowledge each other.

He was a merchant sailor from his early youth. Saying that he had taken too many drugs and slept with too many whores. **"Both'll drive you mad."**

He talks of having seen all of the world, and as big as it is, he knows there is no place for him away from here.

In those first days we dealt in random conversation and requested no information.

I feel we talk mainly for our own benefit, things that we want to say but feel may sound odd voiced to someone else.

Mark knows the value of silver.

I told him about my watch.

I know I can't mention it to anyone else.

It will be translated as confirmation of my madness.

I showed it to him.

I wear it all the time now, its strap is old and threads stick out as though they were chewed. Its true colour is forgotten, banished by its original wearer never having taken it off. Washed, showered and slept with it on their arm.

But whose?

It's not mine.

I have no idea where it came from.

I asked my brother did he put it on me and he said it was on my wrist in the hospital after they found me.

I don't know who put it there or why.

"Does it keep goodtime?" Was all Mark needed to know.

My tale or details beyond question.

I think of telling him other secrets.

As I know they are watching I keep my time outside as brief as bearable. That way they allow me out as often as I like. Nurses tell me how healthy and positive walks are and for them they have a visual confirmation of my progress.

For me it's a pretense that I am not here.

There's a tingling sensation on my cheeks as I go back into the heated air beyond the front door and my elation quickly fades as my empty footsteps fall on lonely stairs.

Maria was out yesterday with her family, they went to the seaside nearby. She has talked so much about it I feel I was there.

Birds flew through the rain and floated out above churning water. Dogs' barked and white foam rode the tops of the waves.

She collected shells, pieces of wood and what she termed pretty things. Filled two plastic carrier bags and brought them back as gifts. She gave me a smooth black stone from the top of the beach near the dunes, told me how she'd really like to have brought me back a wave the moment it broke on the sand.

I told her knowing that she saw and enjoyed it is enough for me.

We were at that beach less than a year ago.

A cold day in early summer.

Paying no heed to the cold we ran from the car and spilt out across the sand. My daughter was afraid of the waves and gathered shells and dead crabs a safe distance and filled her pockets. She reached for a live one in a small rock pool and as it moved towards her she screamed and ran. Convinced her to paddle in the water and she laughed and danced in the sea until her boots were full of water. Her trousers stuck to her legs and her sleeves weighted with the cold sea water hung down over her hands.

As we walked back to the car she felt something moving in her pocket, tried to get away from it. My husband lifted her and held her in his arms as I took the live crab and dropped it onto the sand. Changed into dry clothing we walked to a sand bank and watched seals blubber on their backs. My husband said someone had made a huge mistake when they told the seal they could live out of water.

We camped and all swam until it grew dark and stars appeared in the sky above us and the beach slowly disappeared beneath an incoming tide. We built a fire and her feet were cold and I held them in my hands to warm them up.

Lying in the tent we told stories and fell asleep to the great sound of isolation.

There was a small airstrip nearby and the following morning we stood against a chain link fence and watched planes land and take off. My daughter said she would never get on one and pointed out that like the seals who had told people they could fly?

How easy it was to be happy when we were far from home and I could evade the ghosts that were pursuing and gaining on me.

I got a Mother's day card in the post today.
I don't see her that often anymore as it's hard to watch her leave. It's homemade and my face takes up most of the page and my smile sits proud in pencil. The paper is flimsy and it's impossible to get it to stand so I use it as a book mark.

I love you mammy
If you
Love us all you have to do is sayso and we will believe you
Xxxxxxxx

I make myself read it over and over. It makes me cry and determined to sort myself out, but mostly it makes me feel lonely.

* * *

Jackie went home this morning.
There was a brief time of safety at her side.
She left with her things to catch the bus home. There was no one coming to collect her or waiting to meet her at the bus stop.
I gave her €5 towards a packet of cigarettes.
We exchanged our mobile numbers but I changed one digit on mine.
What use are we to each other away from here?
I miss her and feel lost.
I didn't go for my usual after breakfast walk, paced up and down the corridor counting tiles and going to the toilet. Washing my face and hands for something mindless and repetitive to do. How quickly we become dependent on another's company.
This afternoon I sat in the queue for the chiropodist, not speaking to or even listening to the others around me. When it came to my turn I got up from the chair, leaving the ward to go outside.

I didn't walk, I just sat on a bench thinking how can this place make any difference to my future mind?

Jackie left here still shedding tears at night afraid to go home.

Still sad.

Still knowing that her baby would be crying, her five year old still demanding and her baby's father unable to love her little boy. No amount of rest, talk or pills is going to make people she loves into a family.

Jackie left here today with her high heels on, hair straightened, a prescription and her mascara running.

What hope me?

Outside Mark joined me on the bench and showed me a picture he had torn from a magazine. It was a copy of a black and white photograph of a group of about twenty young men standing in a warehouse of some sort. He asked if I could see anyone standing in the shadows behind the men and if I thought it might be him.

The picture appeared to have been taken a long time before Mark's faring cast him here. I could see no one, but that wasn't the answer he wanted so I told him it was hard to be sure if it was him or not.

Pleased he folded the picture and put it back inside his jacket.

He spat and told me to get the fuck out of here.

Days are passing and I am mastering this reality with pills that make me dream insane dreams, peopled with faces I don't recognise. When I wake it's like trying to fight my way up from under water, gasping and panicking for breath.

Mark is right.

No more tablets.

I must think my own thoughts.

Bono said it was a beautiful day, what the fuck would he know?!

Three

I've stopped the medication

Haven't taken anything for three days and my mind is becoming clearer.

"Don't be fooled into highs." The doctor warned when I told him that I didn't want to take anything.

Told him I only had one question to be answered before I stop taking them.

"Am I coping or is it the tablets?"

"A bit of both."

I sometimes wish this man wasn't so honest.

Said the medication was available to me for a reason.

"You would take an aspirin if you had a headache."

"I don't have that kind of headache."

And so he agrees to let me go it alone, with the option of a pill available if I find things becoming too much, or hear anything I shouldn't.

He says I don't have to wait for nurses to contact him or a colleague as he has left the medication written up and available on request.

He questions me if there is some imagined mental state that I am seeking?

Something that may disappoint me when I realise it doesn't exist outside of my mind.

It's hard to describe what I need.

All I can picture is the sound in a quiet space when everyone is hushed and on the point of holding their breath. Or if you were to flick a glass in an empty room. That's the clarity I crave.

"I don't want to be afraid of the night and the dreams sleep offers."

He listens without interruption.

"Dreams trick me like the trailer for a film.

They entice me to stay in my seat.

Everything is there. All the best bits, my life, the people, the moments that made me laugh, cry and scream."

There is no editing in my nightmares and the same reels play on in what feels like real time.

She will always find me in my sleep.

I need to know that when I hear someone speak, they are real. That I am not their Creator.

* * *

I've started to wear my pajamas in the afternoon to avoid having to go to Occupational Therapy or Relaxation. Patients who have not been given their clothes back are not allowed to be included in either group.

A reasoning that they can't be trusted with a pot of glue and scissors. The therapists are generally students from outside of the unit studying in the main hospital and have no idea who is at what stage of rehabilitation.

For the first few weeks of getting dressed I did take part in both activities but it's too demoralizing playing Snap and making pictures out of scraps of paper.

Now minutes before either group activity I undress and reappear in my night clothes and head to the smoking room.

One of the nurses says she is aware of what I am doing and if I keep it up I should soon be ready to go home.

Maria made an amazing bicycle with coloured drinking straws. The wheels moved as she pushed it along the table and somehow she made a tiny stand that kicked out from the side and allowed the bike to freely stand on the table top.

Relaxation is a tape of ridiculous music and a woman and man with unbearable tones telling you to float above your body. The voices take it in turn to repeat what the other has said.

Such mind games are taken literally by some and they become addicted to the soaring experiences, others snigger, myself included, like children or fall asleep on the foam mattresses and have to be woken when the session ends.

My counsellor says that talking on these pages probably makes better use of my time than the classes but that I mustn't hide amongst the words.

Two student doctors asked me how I thought my daughter would have dealt with my death. I told them that it may be a strange answer but children adapt.

Children's lives are all about dealing with new situations and accept kindness from any quarter.

I can never explain to them or to her, or give adequate justification for what I was prepared to award as a defining childhood marker. That when she was young I took flight, that when she needed me I walked away.

I now have to live with that as well as all the other things to haunt me.

How can I tell how scared each day made me feel?

Always on edge, afraid of being found out or brought back to finish what had been started?

I got up every day and ran through my mind where I would be going.

I feared chance.

Afraid that I would meet my sister or she would call to the house. I would make sure to visit my parents when I knew she was at work.

Her children attend the same school as my daughter and most mornings came by bus. There were days when she worked late and dropped them off on her way. I would leave my house as late as possible sure to avoid her.

One morning she was out of her car as I pulled up and came over to speak to me about our parents wedding anniversary.

I was wearing sunglasses and she told me to take them off when speaking to her.

I did.

I did what I had always done.

Whatever she asked.

I drove home and sat in my car.

I hated myself for doing as she had told me. I cried, my whole body shaking, wanting to get sick, wanting to go back, to have refused and kept the fucking glasses on. Humiliated.

The same humiliation I felt when I remember being made to kneel down on all fours.

I was eager to please.

I did it every time and hated myself more.

Approval and acceptance.

I did as I was told.

Always as I was told.

I held out my hand when the woman from karate bid me to do so I did as she asked.

Four

Mark has convinced himself he has a sexually transmitted disease. He read an article that said an untreated STD can cause insanity and lie dormant for years. Convinced that if they'd test and treat him he could move on.

Told him that Al Capone died from syphilis, which makes him laugh and say about all the really useless stuff everyone knows and that is stacked inside our minds. That without it we'd never have enough things to say to each other.

We all discuss football results and the weather instead of what is really on our minds.

So much wasted time.

He say he knows where his life went wrong. That he should have sorted things out while it could still effect the outcome of other people's lives'.

Tells me he lied to and stole from his mother when he was a young man and that the rest of his family never forgave him.

But she did.

Begged him by letter many times to come and see her.

The loud man in bars and quick with his fists was ultimately a coward and could never face her or even put words on paper.

He swallows back tears and regret.

Lowering his head into laboured breaths of silence.

His mother is in hospital, the General hospital nearby. A red brick building we can see in the distance from where we now sit. She is suffering from Alzheimer's and he is afraid that if he goes to see her she won't recognise who he is and she'll die not knowing that she saw him again.

All he wants is for her to know she was right to love him.

I tell him to go and see her, ask one of the student nurses to bring him over. At least he would have gone and no one could say he didn't say sorry to her or that he wasn't prepared for her to be angry with him.

"They'll say I only went because she hasn't a fucking clue who she is."

"What difference, you'll know."

Smiling, he says that if we could get ourselves fixed between the pair of us;

"We'd sort this fucking place out."

Always easier to give advice than take it."

He laughs.

"That's the reason so many people have jobs here."

I decide to tell him everything.

Selfishly I know that if he talks they will think it is his psychosis and I will laugh if questioned.

"Where did you get it?"

The cross bow belongs to my brother-in-law.

It's illegal to own but someone gave it to him in payment for a debt.

He, my husband and some of their friends used it in the hayshed at our house. Firing into an archery target pinned to a bale of straw. They lost interest but the bale is still in place.

Three graphite arrows that have weight without being heavy came with it. Sleek metallic red with yellow bands creeping up the shaft. I used them to practise.

I had fired a shot gun before and so knew about cushioned resistance against my shoulder. Aware that I had to go with the kick like steering into a skid.

I became an accomplished shot.

You can learn to kill anything from the internet with any weapon of choice. There is someone out there who has planned it, done it, or thought it all through.

Also there is nothing you cannot buy.

Every hunter recommended arrows with razor edge tips and I bought them and paid for express delivery. They were shorter than those I had been using.

I hid the cross bow saying it would be safer if it was put away.

My husband agreed.

I covered it with a blanket.

It's sighted and ready.

As I talked a nurse came over and said my husband had been on the phone and would ring back in ten minutes.

I said goodbye to Mark and followed her back into the building.

There is a three sided booth and a chair at the pay phone and exactly ten minutes later he rang. A child at school had told my daughter that I had got lost and been found at a lake.

She was upset and confused.

Real voices were moving closer, they stooped beneath branches like trackers and beaters as they called out and shook the trees.

Any sound to move my hunted body into sight.

I lifted my head and saw them.

I crawled closer to a tree, pressing my face against its unsmooth surface.

Praying that somehow that they wouldn't see me.

That it wasn't me they were looking for.

Wanting night to come and once again possess me.

Their movements stopped.

Their voices hushed.

They had spotted me.

They edged closer, creeping as though the ground beneath them concealed explosives, weary I might bolt.

Cornered, fearful, small, and feral.

A man I knew said my name and I closed my eyes defeated.

No one came near or touched me.

I heard voices as they talked on mobile phones, different conversations the same words.

"She's alive."

Quickly people gathered, reverently standing back. Their motives unquestionable. They all wore coats and rain gear. Their tired faces starred down at me.

They silently moved en masse to let my parents through. My mother fell on my body and cried. My father stood over her.

My little brother lay down, his body warm next to mine. Rocking and chanting my name over and over.

So many voices.

I wondered would my husband be there.

Two hands pushed in to take hold of mine, I knew his touch, rough skin and long nails.

They all talked at once.

Apart from my father, he said nothing and has been unable to speak to me since.

I had no voice.

I had nothing left to say.

Voices and faces are distorted now in my memory and I can't hear what they all said. Their lips moving their voices quite hushed like church.

From this hospital I wonder how will I face these people on anything level and live amongst them.

Will I thank them?

Branches were cut and held out of the way as I was carried to the waiting ambulance.

I was pushed inside, wrapped in foil and blankets.

Questions, questions.

My hands and feet were cold and I heard a paramedic say something about the body restricting blood supply to protect itself.

Each time I closed my eyes they spoke to me and I looked up and saw the sky through the window.

She had been there when they found me.

Standing back with others when the stretcher pashed through the door of the ambulance. The only prayer ever answered as she didn't come anywhere near to me.

She knew.

She knew why.

Later my brother told me that she had asked to see my note.

My husband held it.

Five

Days are getting harder and I fear I am not going to change, not going to show progress. I worry about having to remain here.
To play this game forever.
Jackie said she thought this had been her fourth or fifth time here.
Each time vowing never again.
As much as I see being here as a waste of time, just a delay on what is still to come. What am I going to do, I have changed, and everything has changed.
Changed without changing at all.
No pieces moved.

The counsellor asked me to draw two pictures. One a happy time, the other of something that evokes sadness and hurt. I joked that I couldn't draw, she said it wasn't an art class and it doesn't have to be anything, just images that represent a high and a low.
To have meaning to me.
I think and remain silent for a time, already beginning to feel edgy and unsure.
I ask can I just put colours and she nods.
Feeling stupid I kneel on the floor two sheets of drawing paper in front of me.
I begin.
No thought to colour or a plan.
Before me a bright blue cloudless sky, simple yellow sun beaming from its corner.

I glance towards the empty sheet already intimidated by the knowledge of the colours it will show.

I continue, a darker blue for a lake where I swam with my daughter, green grass and a patch of pink for the duvet we picnicked on daily and began to smell from drying in the sun, soaked from wet feet and bodies. Rolled up every evening into the boot of the car. That too began to smell like a wet dog. The duvet thrown on the hedge over night to get the early morning rays of the sun.

I tell her of the days we spent swimming and eating and being happy with friends or on our own till late evening. Going home and coming back for night swims with her father.

I push the paper away, I feel ill as my fingers pull the blank sheet towards me.

I take two colours, orange and brown and swirl round and round. Going faster and faster.

Harder.

The crayons etching the texture of the carpet underneath the paper.

It tears in places.

I panic and start to cry.

Ask her to let me leave.

"Please."

Still I force the crayons over and back.

"Tell me what you've drawn?"

I quickly explain that it is the carpet on the floor of the room the first time she touched me.

I stand. **"Please I can't stay here."**

She opens the door and walks with me down the corridor as far as the water dispenser where we realise that I have left my shoes on the floor. She tells me to take a drink and wait, she will go back and get them.

Seated in the hallway she told me that back in that room fear and grief were present and harsh.

She didn't want to remain any longer than she had to.

Felt the paper brazenly goad her.

We walk back to my bed and she explains that she may not see me again before my targeted release date but will be working with me as often as I feel up to it when I go home.

She apologises for what had just taken place and hopes that I don't feel she has pushed me backwards.

"There is something I want you to picture in your head, when we met, what you told me and what you have drawn are now left in that room.

Leave them and their power there."

She gives me her mobile number and says if I need her she's always at the other end.

She leaves.

I lie on the bed, my head under the blankets. A nurse comes and asks how the session went. I am aware of her and pretend to sleep.

What am I going to do?

Leave it in the room.

Another image for me to contend with.

All my demons are now gathered in that room, just another extension of my mind that I can't forget.

When I was in my early teens I was taken to the family doctor because of how I felt. Lethargic and uninterested.

He gave me tablets.

I lay on my bed and I heard them laughing in the kitchen as my mother told my father and sister that I was suffering from nervous exhaustion.

They all laughed.

She laughed.

I wrote a letter to my mother over the following days to try and explain how I felt.

She told me they read it, my sister said I spent too much time on my own.

She had given it to my sister to read.

Nothing was different with the pills and I still climbed the stairs.

Our bodies had changed.

Sometimes she just wanted to look.

I'd pull down my pants so that she could see my emergent pubic hair.

I'd hold up my tee shirt.

She'd sit on the edge of the bed and bend forward almost touching her face to my body, her breath warm on my skin.

I'd tuck my tee shirt under my chin and move my waist and hips in a circular motion. My own fingers reaching down and trailing over my thighs.

I hated this more than her touch.

She'd turn out the lights and get into bed first. Telling me to pull my pants back up and take everything else off.

Now when we lay there she said very little to me.

I was glad, I didn't want to listen to her words, to her betrayal.

Everything was different now, she didn't disguise what we were doing as a game and no longer did my brother take part.

It was just us.

There was need involved in her movements.

I'd lie on my back as she would move my pants down my legs.

She had warned me to keep my legs tight together until she pulled them apart.

"Fight!" She would urge, her forearm across my throat pressuring her weight down upon me.

I didn't.

She never attempted to kiss me and I think she knew I would re-sist.

She'd manoeuvre me onto my side.

I always complied, the sooner it was over the better.

She'd remove her clothes.

With her hands around my waist she'd pull me closer.

Her knee would rest on my leg and then she'd twist herself closer.

I'd feel her wetness as she'd pant and stifle ugly sounds in her throat.

The smell of sweat as her fingers drove deeper into both of us and I'd cry as I felt my body reacting to her movements.

Finished we'd lie side by side.

I'd leave the room in the dark and walk downstairs into a light that didn't care.

* * *

The air changes here, friction between Patients moves through the corridors and stumbles against walls.

It strikes back with a sudden smack.

Out in the corridor a row breaks out.

Angered voices capture the hour.

I try to assign faces and loyalties.

The shouting blurs to a familiar noise.

I lie on my bed body shaking, try to imagine I cannot hear the glass in our door breaking and the shouting that follows.

Always shouting.

There's a screech, a horrible sound that one can't imagine can possibly come from within a human soul.

People running doors banging.

I followed the scent.

In the corridor we fought with each other to get a better view of the girl with the scratches and bloodied mouth as she writhed on the floor, nurses hold her down.

Maria covers her mouth afraid to inhale what has been released.

Another nurse and a doctor work on a woman with a sleeve of a jumper wrapped around her neck, secured like a ribbon on a child's present.

They call her name.

I run.

Wishing to disappear to be hidden to be gone.

As though coming up from underground I hear sounds and realise I hear a drill.

A sheet of ply is being fixed into the door where the glass is no longer.

The darkness surrounding me is from the duvet where I sought refuge.

Sounds are quickly recycled and a sedated mind taken to Special Care.

No one talks about what has happened.

Six

After they took me from the ambulance to the room that was waiting for me in Accident and Emergency my husband put his head on my chest and asked were things really that bad between us.

I whispered, still too frightened to tell, to reassure him it wasn't his fault.

Despite all the confusion my mind knew in that moment that I had lost him.

His love from now on governed differently.

He later told me angrily that he could understand me leaving him but not our daughter.

Guilty as charged.

That first night is random and blurred. I was cleaned up. I was examined by a doctor who held my arms to show another doctor what appeared to be old scaring above the fresh cuts.

I turned my head as they talked.

During the summer before I finished school I worked in a quiet bar and most days saw few customers.

At that time most nights my sister waited for me to get home.

I had a small paring knife with a bright orange handle. I carried it in my handbag all the time. I would sit on a stool, take the knife from my bag and run it over and back across my skin. Each time with a little more pressure.

Once I saw blood I stopped.

Pulled down my sleeve and put the knife away.

The material would cause my wrist to sting and I would have to wait for it to heal before cutting again. This time a little further up. I tried to keep both arms at the same state.

My sister noticed and said I was mad.

One day a salesman passed boxes of crisps across the counter. He held onto my arm and looked at the red scabby trail. He released me and asked had I a fight with a cat.

I said nothing, panicked inside that he would tell the people I worked for and my parents would find out. He threw a couple of bags onto the counter and said they were for me and to take care of myself.

Those scabby lines are now white smooth sketches fading up my forearms.

I couldn't walk because of the mixture of tablets I had taken and I hovered in a haze. The anti-coagulant I'd been daily overdosing on was taking effect and the vitamin K injection was finding it hard to perform antidote magic.

I couldn't tell them how much I had taken in the proceeding days as I didn't know.

I spoke little,

I wouldn't tell.

As I slept my wrists began to bleed, the sheets soaking a deep red. I woke but said nothing. Falling back to sleep, to be roused when a member of the night staff noticed.

I was given plasma, one arm suspended in a sling to help stop the bleeding.

I was placed in an isolation ward, a carer to sit at my bedside at all times.

I heard a nurse talking when she thought I was asleep saying they weren't equipped to deal with idiots like me.

When I was able to walk unaided the bathroom door was left open so I could be seen. It was feared the wounds on my arms would re-open and so the carer helped me to wash.

The sitters changed three times a day.

Some of them talked to me.

One of them I vaguely knew as the cousin of the boy my friend had met that Sunday when we were young. She made me laugh with stories of her husband, children, work colleagues and how fat and ugly a man my friends dream date had become.

"You'd want a see him now.

Bald and single."

We snuck down to smoke when nurses were busy with their rounds. She brought me hot chocolate at bedtime on the nights she wasn't assigned to me.

I can't forget her simple kindness.

Some viewed me as sort of dangerous and made sure the door to the main corridor was propped open and couldn't fall shut. One was a student and asked if I minded if she read her class work.

My daughter came with my husband to see me.

She said people were talking about me in whispers and that she thought I was never coming back.

I pulled the sleeves of my dressing gown over the bandages. I had no explanation.

"Where were you?"

Said I had gone to clear my head, that it had got dark and couldn't find my way back to the car.

"Don't go again."

My husband watched football on a small television high on the wall and my daughter climbed in beside me and we talked of unreal things.

The following day he came back alone and said everyone was talking about what possible reason could have driven me to attempt suicide.

I asked him did he love me.

"If I didn't I wouldn't be here." He laughed unsurely and held me.

We still weren't talking.

The words on my note screamed between us and we let this one brief opportunity of intimacy seep back into the nothingness.

I knew he would never ask me to talk about what I had been through, and I would never venture to tell him.

Both now shutting our eyes and counting to ten.

My sister also cried at my bedside.

And like a child I hid my head beneath a pillow.

"Go away go away go away." I didn't say.

So much easier to let her speak.

To let her win again.

Allow the faults to be hidden beneath the flimsy paper pattern of our family deceits.

I couldn't betray the child I had been, not this time. I lifted the pillow and told her to go home to her children. Teach them her games if she really believes they are harmless.

Ask them how wretched it feels.

* * *

I went home for a morning.

I wanted to say goodbye to my daughter but it was decided it would be too upsetting for both of us and she was elsewhere.

I stood in here room and said goodbye.

I checked that the windows were shut.

There was an evident trace of her in the room.

Her possessions and smells as individual as her.

I said sorry to her games and books and promised to try harder and come home.

Sat in the car as we drove away, I could see the wall of the house needed painting and listed white emulsion somewhere in my future.

That morning four months ago brought me here.

Seven

Like dust expelled from cushions we move around outside on the front lawn.

It's a beautiful November day, warm and caring. A pet day I remembered my father calling these aberrations.

Margaret is in the mood to tell funny stories and waits for reaction then adds a wicked lurid twist. Our responses prompt her to tell more. She tells me that I have a great hearty laugh.

Nan and Maria link arms and head for a walk. The unseen power of the day lifting something from us all.

Glancing I imagine how we must be viewed.

Characters fallen from the rapidly flicked pages of a comic book.

Margaret says she has to go inside and comb her hair as her daughter will be here soon. Her daughter comes every day and hugs her mother with love and pride. There is nothing laboured or dutiful in their relationship What the Margaret before here must have been to have inspired such devotion.

I ask her how long has she been here.

She holds up her hands.

She counts moving her fingers

"One, two, three, four, five, six years.

They'd let me go home if I'd stop shouting."

She whispers. **"I can't."**

Mark asks can he sit beside me.

He looks redrawn, as if a regenerating spotlight has been flicked upon him. He appears to have unwound the stagnant folds of depression from his body. Even the creases in his clothes appear to have vanished.

What a strange day.

He's happy and at ease, was brought to the hospital to visit his mother.

She didn't know him and he didn't tell her who he was. They talked and she told him of her son that had left many years before and that she had never seen him since. She said how much she missed him. How much she still loves him and that he is also called Mark. Before he left she asked Mark to give her son a message if they ever crossed paths.

"Tell him he'll always be my boy."

Instantly his words skip and he tells me about the Alamo. About the Mexicans winning by the simple fact that they stayed awake when Davey Crocket and the soldiers slept.

Marks warns me to stay awake.

I decide to venture further along the path to the old hospital. I am not supposed to go there, it is beyond the boundaries but I don't care. Its silence has beckoned me since I came here. Since I first looked out a window. I walk closer to it each time I walk and I know it waits certain that I will come. My thoughts move towards it frequently when I return to the ward.

I walk beyond the view of the cameras and signs that state.

PRIVATE PROPERTY.

NO TRRESSPASSING.

Further along another sign declares it is a building site and no unauthorised access or admittance. There are no workers and no sounds of industry or construction come from within or near its walls. I have not seen anything that would suggest the proposed luxury hotel is pupating ahead of me.

The huge building appears to rise like a House of Usher before me, and I stand speechless at its sheer size. A building with a past not ready to be forgotten. Everything about it leaves the onlooker in no doubt that they are small and powerless. Six floors of windows.

Windows fronted by metal bars to remind everyone who looked out from within that the view belonged to someone else.

I wonder how many ghosts wander here and did any former inmates find happiness.

It feels as though even in its abandoned and derelict state it demands obedience. Despite being empty for some years vandalism has been minimal.

Possibly fear imparted by reputation.

At the back of the building I see through windows that some had been inventive and built a skateboard ramp from wooden paneling in a gutted open space. Sprayed graffiti and their names. The only evidence of some who gained entry, the abandoned aerosol cans. Pitiful leftovers of the Spinnies. An almost delightful name for a dangerous high. Glue bags vile odour and wrinkled shapes blistered the dirty ground in chaotic waste and I felt this place delivered no true happiness to any who spent time here.

Walking away I pass a small chapel separate from the main building. The doors are padlocked and the windows too high for me to see inside. A woman who had been a patient along with me, an alcoholic, who had spent a week drying out. Sat with me at the window of the smoking room, glimpses of this place visible through trees, and talked about her time here as a patient.

Said her family and a concerned parish priest had placed her there because she was too fond of a good time.

"I liked boys, I liked any company... I didn't drink then."

She said as time passed she became very devout and attended mass every day.

"Prayed and blessed myself like an ejit."

She began to hear a voice, a man's voice.

All through her schooling she'd listened to teachers, priests, and the ones that came back from the missions in Africa. Retreats organised when the returning priests were in the parish and they rattled on about God's calling.

"A Vocation they called it. There would be no doubts, God's intentions clear.

If he wanted you he spoke directly to you.

Do not be afraid."

She told the doctors about the voice and her wish to dedicate her life to the church.

"I believed it was God…….. Should have kept that to myself."

Kneeling in the chapel one morning two nurses came for her.

Said they would make the voices stop.

She was given her first session of ECT.

She couldn't remember how many she got but can remember after the first time not wanting to ever go back inside a church.

The voice ceased.

"But I never stopped hearing myself cry."

She said the old hospital was a scary place, the patients too.

The noise of the demented and hopeless a constant sound like a barely audible hum.

The long corridors, the darkness the cold, always cold.

The sun never shone through the windows or heated the glass.

The loneliness.

The building.

Said those that planned and built it had taken great care with how it looked.

It mattered, it had to be imposing, cut stone and arched windows.

Craftsmanship and detail making it beyond the experiences of those unfortunates who found themselves locked within.

Looking up at it I believe it is not deserted but avoided.

I don't want to remain any longer, my curiosity sated and I know I will soon be missed, someone will have seen or reported my transgression.

Walking back to the new hospital built in the early seventies, it seems like a poor relation, almost apologetic for taking the name of its grandiose predecessor. Mass concrete and flat felt roofs.

There is no one left outside. It is nearing tea time. Routines. Routine rules our lives and nobody wants to miss any important milestone for marking the passage of our day.

Some are already heading into the dining room and along the corridor little groups await all of their members.

The smell announces this evening's fare.

I head to my room to put a jumper on as its cooler indoors.

"What are you doing?"

I don't want the answer.

Maria spins around, my bedside locker open. I feel as though I have been hit hard in the stomach.

"Getting the price of a phone call... knew you'd give it to me but you weren't here when I thought about it.
Want to ring home after tea."

I tell her to go away.

She flings the coins on the bed like rice at a wedding and pushes me as though I have done something wrong.

Pull the curtain around my space and lie down on the bed the coins beneath and beside me still where they fell.

Inside my mind the world shakes and doors bang.

Everything crashes to the ground, spins and shatters.

"Go away go away go away." I say to no body and to everyone.

I hear myself crying unlike any time before.

A nurse comes to me and I cry and I talk and talk.

She picks up the coins. Leaving them down on the locker. When she leaves to get me a cup of coffee I gather them and throw them into a draw out of my sight. I don't want them. Before the nurse leaves she reminds me of the offer of a sleeping tablet

"Maybe a little escape?"

I cannot believe Maria betrayed my trust.

Why didn't she just wait to ask me? I would have gladly given the money to her.

As evening moves on the sounds of the routines deployed to greet the unyielding night pervade the rooms and corridors around me.

Nan calls.

"Are you ok Kathleen?

I don't answer.

"I'm sorry for whatever has made you sad. Goodnight."

I feel bad for not answering her the first time and call out goodnight to her.

Tomorrow I will talk to any of them who want to hear me. I will comply, swallow their tablets, breathe deeply, fold paper and go home.

I don't sleep.

I relive all I wish to forget.

So many things I never wanted to do.

"Pretend I am your boyfriend."

The woman at karate said as we lay down on the foam mat.

She was naked as was I.

I lay at her side my head resting on her arm and my hand across her stomach.

"Hold me tighter."

Asked me his name.

I didn't have a boyfriend but thought of a poster on the back of my cousins bedroom door of David Cassidy.

"I'll be David." Her open mouth covered mine and our hands moved.

I never told.

I know why children never tell.

Because they know.

Know that ornaments can't be moved out of place.

Know that voices must be kept low, hushed, better still, seen and never heard.

No never heard.

That sleeping dogs notoriously love and need their rest.

And children know that anyone can be traded.

It was my parents who brought my sister to my hospital room.

"To sort this out." My mother said. My father at her side, both standing with their backs to the door.

I pleaded with them to take my sister out.

My mother said no.

Said I had to listen to what my sister had to say.

No where can I remember being granted that judgment.

I pulled the pillow over my head, covering ears and eyes and I cried.

She still had the upper hand.

She began to speak. She remembered all the things just as I had.

She had never forgotten any of the places we were.

My parents heard those words and I realised it didn't matter what my sister had done or if they had known.

They'd never forsake or believe ill even when she herself presented it to them.

Words, words, she talked.

I knew there wasn't anyone back then or now to help me.

No one was going to make it stop.

The Brown Lady lifted the pillow and I was eight years old.

My sister was sobbing **"I'm not proud of what I did, but it was a long time ago."**

My heart beat to escape, if I could follow it and be gone, an echo

The little girl that I had been pinched me to move, begged me to speak.

My whole body trembled and a woman who wasn't there or real cried at my side. The muscles of my legs pained and I spoke.

I told her to go home, that I wasn't going to make her feel better.

No absolution.

Told her she had children go home and teach them her games.

She was silent and listening to me.

I got out of bed and began to scream. Stood in front of my parents and said I would throw myself out of a window if they didn't get her out of the room.

They just looked at me. No words. No movement.

My sister stood.

She knew I was still afraid of her and I knew that if she didn't leave I would back down and cower forever.

"Mammy!" I pleaded.

"You did it too." Her eyes were dry and her face set in defiance.

She left the room, and my mother chased after her.

My father lowered his head and was gone.

I remained at the window, my mother came back to collect her purse, still crying and I put my arms around her. She said her whole life had been a lie, that she always knew I hated my sister.

She never asked why.

She made no comment on what she had heard.

Each of my family has tentatively made reference to what was written in my note. Questioning is it the truth and am I sure. Even now they haven't stood up and said they heard what she said.

A vindictive fantasist her husband called me.

It doesn't really matter.

At least she knows that I haven't forgotten.

* * *

Jackie said it was time to go home when it wasn't funny here anymore. I know what she meant.

I saw my husband outside yesterday day in the car park. I watched the door but he never came in and when I checked the car was gone.

I know it was for a meeting with doctors to see if I am ready to go home, and if he is ready for me to go back.

Eight

<u>I am going home.</u>
Kathleen still doesn't know when she will leave here. I told her I'd come and visit but she said she hoped I'd never come back, not even to visit.
I see my daughter stepping from the car, her hair like a banner broadcasting that her father got her ready.
I hope I can match the happiness her movements feel.
I have to tell her to hang on to her happy memories, as they have to last a lifetime.
And the good ones are all that makes life bearable.

I lied,
I did tell.
I told my mother that my vagina was sore.
She asked me where I had heard that word.
From my sister.
Told me never to use it again.

But I also lied when I told the doctor that I no longer hear voices.
That when we had talked I had told him everything.
I didn't tell and I hadn't forgotten those who had crawled into the night at my home.
They were predictable.

There is no way after the bolt has been fired from a crossbow that it can be stopped from hitting the target.

Not unless you shout at him to move.

But I wouldn't do that.

I wanted, meant to kill him.

As the tip and shaft passed through his throat I knew for certain that he would die.

For a moment I think he believed it was a joke. Like getting hit by a paper pellet fired from an elastic band catapult.

It stings.

His body surrendered to my truth.

First his knees gave and down he slid. His hands tugging in panic at the arrow aiding its damage. Blood steadily flowed over his skin. It didn't spurt as I had imagined. No explosion of red. The wound opened in silence. He would choke, drown on his own blood.

I stepped back into the dark, the lights from the Takeaway illuminated his dying form.

The other one appeared out through the doorway and said something to his friend, no doubt thinking he had fallen asleep, drunk. Clutching a brown paper bag he moved closer to the trembling heap. He leaned down then shot up as though tapped on the shoulder.

The lights in the Takeaway went out.

He banged on the door, but they ignored him, he was predictable. He kicked their door late at night and shouted abuse. I lifted the bow, hit him, piercing his heart through his back. A kill shot.

I wished them a good night and sat into my car.

I could no longer hear any voices and sang along to late night radio.

THE END

Til Sigrun. "Takk fyrir mig fyrir einu sinni var."
First draft readers. "R" "R.P" "J" & "N"
You know who you are. Thank you.
You've started something now.

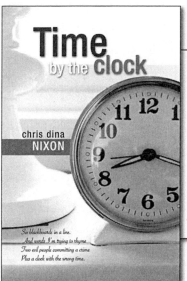

Time
by the **clock**

chris dina
NIXON

Six blackboards in a line.
And words I'm trying to rhyme.
Two evil people committing a crime
Plus a clock with the wrong time.

Their day arrives in the dark, bringing realisation that the movements on a clock are irrelevant to the outcome of life.

Catherine and the young girl haven't slept. They are complete strangers but Catherine clings to the cold child and wonders what to pray for.

Time to stop or End?

Available in:
Printed format (80pp €9.30)
eBook Formats €3.99)

publishedinireland.com
BOOKS WRITTEN AND PUBLISHED IN IRELAND

// BOOKSTORE

www.publishedinireland.com

Designed, typeset, printed and bound in Ireland by

PubliBook Ireland
www.publibookireland.com

PubliBook IRELAND